TOPICS
IN
MODERN
ALGEBRA

HARPER'S MATHEMATICS SERIES

Charles A. Hutchinson, Editor

TOPICS IN MODERN ALGEBRA

CHARLES P. BENNER   *University of Houston*

ALBERT NEWHOUSE   *University of Houston*

CORTEZ B. RADER   *University of Houston*

RICHARD L. YATES   *Kansas State University*

HARPER & ROW, PUBLISHERS

New York, Evanston, and London

512
B469

TOPICS IN MODERN ALGEBRA

Copyright © 1962 by Harper & Row, Publishers, Incorporated,
Printed in the United States of America

Library of Congress catalog card number: 62-7430

Contents

Preface

Since the traditional theory of equations course is rapidly being eliminated from the mathematics curriculum, a need has developed for a course which introduces selected topics in abstract algebra and at the same time retains some essential results from the theory of equations. The authors feel that the text for such a course should provide a transition from the concrete problem-solving approach to an abstract presentation. With these needs in mind, the authors have sought to write a text which will provide a foundation for further study in abstract algebra as well as in allied fields.

A preliminary version of the material has been used for several semesters at the University of Houston in a course for students who had completed elementary calculus.

This text is designed for a one-year course meeting three hours per week. We have found that in one semester the first seven chapters can be covered. Although most of the chapters are somewhat dependent on preceding chapters, there is some flexibility in the order of presentation. For example, Chapter VI depends only on Chapter V, and both may be postponed without disturbing the continuity. Although the exercises are not necessary for continuity, they contain many supplementary results.

In order to avoid the unfortunate confusion between matrices and determinants which frequently arises in the student's mind, we have developed the elements of matrix theory and its application to the solution of linear equations without recourse to determinants. By the time determinants are defined in Chapter XII, the student should have sufficient familiarity with matrices to be able to distinguish between the two concepts.

TOPICS
IN
MODERN
ALGEBRA

CHAPTER I

Foundations

INTRODUCTION

Any mathematical discussion is concerned with *undefined terms* and *defined terms*. For example, the student has a clear intuitive understanding of the meaning of the undefined term "number." On the other hand, the term "square of a number" is well defined by means of the undefined term "number" and the defined operation "multiplication."

A *mathematical system* consists of a *set of elements*, *relations* among its elements, *operations* on its elements, *postulates*, *definitions*, and *theorems*. We shall accept the undefined term "set" in its intuitive meaning of a collection, group, or class of "elements," which is itself an undefined term. Relations and operations will be discussed in subsequent sections. The postulates are statements concerning the elements, relations, and operations of the system. These postulates are assumed to be valid for the system and they form a basis from which further properties can be developed. These deduced properties are called theorems.

To illustrate, consider the familiar set of positive integers. We define the predecessor (successor) of an element of the set to be that element which immediately precedes (succeeds) the given element in numerical order. We postulate that every element has a successor but not necessarily a predecessor. With additional postulates we can prove that the set contains exactly one element which has no predecessor.

Henceforth we shall use capital script letters ($\mathscr{A}$, $\mathscr{B}$, $\mathscr{C}$, ...) to denote mathematical systems and capital italic letters (A, B, C, ...) to denote sets.

RELATIONS

A relation can be concerned with any number of elements. For example, on the set of all integers, the relation "is the square of itself" involves only one element. On the same set, "is greater than" is a relation between two elements. On the set of all points in a plane, "are collinear" is a relation involving two or more points.

However, the most frequently encountered relations are those involving two elements, and we restrict our discussion to these relations.

▶DEFINITION 1.1. If, for any a and b in a set A of elements, either a is in relation R to b or a is not in relation R to b, then R is a *binary relation* on A.

Some examples of binary relations on the set of integers are "is equal to," "is less than," "is a multiple of," and "is a divisor of." Binary relations frequently have one or more of the following properties:

1. A binary relation R on A is *reflexive* if a R a (a in relation R to a) for *all a* in A.
2. A binary relation R on A is *symmetric* if a R b implies b R a for *all a, b* in A.
3. A binary relation R on A is *transitive* if a R b and b R c implies a R c for *all a, b, c* in A.

For example, on the set of all human beings the binary relation "lives in the same house as" is reflexive, symmetric, and transitive, whereas "is older than" is transitive but not reflexive or symmetric, and "is father of" has none of the three properties.

Similarly, on the set of all integers the binary relation " $\leq$ " is reflexive and transitive, whereas "is the square of" is neither reflexive, symmetric, nor transitive.

On the set of all polygons the binary relation "has the same number of vertices as" has all three properties.

▶DEFINITION 1.2. A binary relation on the set A which is reflexive, symmetric, and transitive is an *equivalence relation* on A.

It is easily verified that congruence as well as similarity on triangles is an equivalence relation.

▶DEFINITION 1.3. For any integers a, b, and m, $a \equiv b$ (mod m) [read: a congruent to b modulo m] means $a - b$ is an integral multiple of m.

Note that $a \equiv b$ (mod m) if and only if $a \equiv b$ (mod $-m$). Hence there is no loss of generality in assuming m to be nonnegative.

▶THEOREM 1.1. Congruency for a fixed modulus m is an equivalence relation on the set of all integers.

PROOF: Congruence modulo m is a binary relation which obviously has the reflexive and symmetric properties. To show transitivity, assume $a \equiv b$ (mod m) and $b \equiv c$ (mod m), that is, $a - b = km$ and $b - c = hm$. Adding, we obtain $a - c = (h + k)m$, and thus $a \equiv c$ (mod m).

We observe that $a \equiv b$ (mod 0) if and only if $a = b$. Thus congruence modulo 0 is equivalent to equality. Furthermore, any two integers are congruent modulo 1.

▶DEFINITION 1.4. If R is an equivalence relation on A and a is any element of A, then the *equivalence class* R_a is the subset of all elements b of A such that b R a.

▶THEOREM 1.2. With respect to an equivalence relation R on A, every element in A belongs to one and only one distinct equivalence class.

PROOF: If a is in R_b, then all elements of R_b are equivalent to b and hence equivalent to a. Thus R_a and R_b are identical.

An alternative statement of Theorem 1.2 is that an equivalence relation R on A separates A into a totally exhaustive set of mutually exclusive subsets. For example, the equivalence relation "congruent modulo 2" separates the integers into the familiar subsets of even and odd integers.

Similarly, the equivalence relation "is similar to" on the set of all triangles leads to classes in which all triangles in the same class have the same angles.

The set of all integers congruent modulo m leads to equivalence classes. Since congruence modulo 0 results in equivalence classes containing only one integer and congruence modulo 1 results in a single equivalence class, these cases are uninteresting. Henceforth we shall restrict ourselves to $m > 1$.

Consider the equivalence class $\{a\}_m$ of integers congruent to $a \pmod m$. Since a divided by m gives an integral quotient and q an integral remainder i such that $0 \le i < m$, we have $a = qm + i$. Thus $a \equiv i \pmod m$. But any other integer in the same class is congruent to $a \pmod m$ and hence by transitivity is congruent to $i \pmod m$. Thus every integer in $\{a\}_m$ is of the form $km + i$ for some $k(k = \ldots, -2, -1, 0, 1, 2, \ldots)$. Thus $\{a\}_m = \{i\}_m$ and we shall call i the *representative* of this class. Thus the totality of equivalence classes modulo m is represented by the integers $0, 1, 2, \ldots, (m-1)$.

We shall define addition and multiplication of equivalence classes as follows: $\{a\}_m + \{b\}_m = \{a + b\}_m$ and $\{a\}_m\{b\}_m = \{ab\}_m$. Wherever possible we shall use representatives in lieu of equivalence classes. For example, for the modulus 5 the addition and multiplication tables are given in Table 1.1.

The system consisting of the set of all equivalence classes modulo m, together with the operations of addition and multiplication defined above, will be denoted by $\mathscr{I}_m$.

Exercise 1.1. Which of the following binary relations on the set

TABLE 1.1.   Addition and Multiplication in $\mathscr{J}_5$

+	0	1	2	3	4
0	0	1	2	3	4
1	1	2	3	4	0
2	2	3	4	0	1
3	3	4	0	1	2
4	4	0	1	2	3

×	0	1	2	3	4
0	0	0	0	0	0
1	0	1	2	3	4
2	0	2	4	1	3
3	0	3	1	4	2
4	0	4	3	2	1

of all positive integers are reflexive? Symmetric? Transitive? Equivalence relations?

    a. Is equal to.

    b. Is less than.

    c. Is a multiple of.

    d. Is a divisor of.

Exercise 1.2. Which of the following binary relations on the set of all people at one particular moment are reflexive? Symmetric? Transitive? Equivalence relations?

    a. Is a resident of the same nation as.

    b. Is a parent of.

    c. Is an ancestor of.

    d. Belongs to the same family as.

    e. Is not younger than.

    f. Is the same age as.

Exercise 1.3. Describe the equivalence classes for those relations in Exercise 1.2 which are equivalence relations.

Exercise 1.4. Write the addition and multiplication tables for $\mathscr{J}_2$, $\mathscr{J}_6$, and $\mathscr{J}_7$.

Exercise 1.5. If $a \equiv c \pmod{m}$ and $b \equiv d \pmod{m}$, prove that $a + b \equiv c + d \pmod{m}$ and $ab \equiv cd \pmod{m}$.

OPERATIONS

The concept of "operation" is based upon that of "mapping." Mappings are special types of correspondences. Some examples of correspondences occurring in everyday life are (1) books in a library to cards in its card catalogue, (2) members of a history class to names, (3) driver's licenses to drivers, (4) names to people, (5) books to library call numbers.

▶DEFINITION 1.5. A *correspondence* from a set A to a set B is a rule which assigns at least one element of the set B to each element of the set A.

Consider the set of 30 people in a college class and the set of 5 grades A, B, C, D, and F, assuming that each grade is assigned to at least one person. Taking the set A of the definition as the set of students and the set B as the set of grades, to each element of set A there corresponds a unique element of set B. Taking set A as the set of grades and set B as the set of students, to some of the elements of set A there must correspond more than one element of set B. Nevertheless, both of these are examples of correspondences. However, removing the assumption that each grade is assigned to at least one person and assuming that no one failed, we still have a correspondence from persons to grades in spite of the fact that one element of set B is not assigned to any element of set A. On the other hand, since the grade F is not assigned to any person, we do not have a correspondence from the set of grades to the set of students. However, we still have a correspondence from the subset of grades A, B, C, and D to the set of persons.

▶**DEFINITION 1.6.** A correspondence from a set A to a set B in which no two elements of A have the same element of B assigned to them and in which every element of B is assigned to one and only one element of A is a *one-to-one correspondence*.

An example of a one-to-one correspondence is the correspondence from the set of states in the United States to the set of names of these states and vice versa.

Exercise 1.6. Which of the correspondences in examples 1 through 5 (preceding Definition 1.5) are correspondences if the sets in each example are interchanged? Which of these are one-to-one correspondences?

Exercise 1.7. If there is a one-to-one correspondence from set A to set B, prove that there is a one-to-one correspondence from set B to set A. (This is called the *inverse correspondence*.)

▶**DEFINITION 1.7.** A *mapping* F of a set A into a set B is a correspondence which assigns to every element of a set A a unique element b of the set B. Symbolically, $a\mathrm{F} = b$.

The correspondences people to their day of birth and social security numbers to people are both mappings. The first is an example of a many-to-one mapping, whereas the latter is an example of a one-to-one mapping.

▶**DEFINITION 1.8.** The *Cartesian product* of set A and set B, denoted by $A \times B$, is the set of all ordered pairs (a,b) where a is a member of A and b is a member of B.

As an example, let the elements of set A be 0, 1, 3 and the elements of set B be 2 and 4. The Cartesian product $A \times B$ is the set having for elements the six ordered pairs: (0,2), (0,4), (1,2), (1,4), (3,2), (3,4).

▶**DEFINITION 1.9.** A *closed binary operation on a set A* is a mapping of $A \times A$ into A.

We shall denote operations in general by symbols $\bigcirc$, ①, ②, etc.; and when (a,b) maps into c, we shall write $a \bigcirc b = c$.

In a strict sense Definition 1.9 defines a closed binary operation on a set A, that is, an operation on two elements of the set A resulting in an element of the set A. However, since we shall be dealing almost entirely with closed binary operations, we shall refer to them as "operations on a set" or, where no confusion can arise, simply as "operations."

A familiar example of an operation is addition on the set of positive integers; the sum $2 + 3 = 5$ is a mapping of the ordered pair (2,3) into the element 5.

Exercise 1.8. Let the elements of A be a, b, and c and the elements of B be x, y, and z. List the elements of $A \times B$.

Exercise 1.9. If A contains m elements and B contains n elements, how many elements are there in $A \times B$?

Exercise 1.10. Given the following sets:

1. All even integers.
2. All odd integers.

3. All integers.
4. All rational numbers.
5. All real numbers.
6. All complex numbers.
7. All rational numbers of the form $1/n$, where n is a nonzero integer.

Which of the following are operations on these sets: (*a*) addition, (b) multiplication, (c) subtraction, (d) division?

BASIC PROPERTIES OF OPERATIONS

In addition to the property of closure inherent in the definition of an operation, there are other important properties which these operations may possess.

►**DEFINITION 1.10.** *Commutativity.* An operation is *commutative* on a set A if $a \bigcirc b = b \bigcirc a$ for every a and b in A.

On the set of all integers the operation of addition is commutative, whereas that of subtraction is not.

►**DEFINITION 1.11.** *Associativity.* An operation is *associative* on a set A if $a \bigcirc (b \bigcirc c) = (a \bigcirc b) \bigcirc c$ for every a, b, and c in A.

On the set of all integers addition is associative, whereas subtraction is not.

►**DEFINITION 1.12.** An element e in A such that $a \bigcirc e = e \bigcirc a = a$ for every a in A is called an *identity element* for the operation $\bigcirc$.

Let A be the set of all rational numbers; then 0 is the identity element for addition and 1 is the identity element for multiplication, but there is no identity element among the rational numbers for the operation of subtraction.

►**DEFINITION 1.13.** If for an element a belonging to the set A there exists an element b belonging to A such that $a \bigcirc b = b \bigcirc a = e$, where e is the identity element for the operation $\bigcirc$, then b is the *inverse* of a with respect to $\bigcirc$.

If A is the set of all rational numbers, then $-a$ is the inverse of the element a of A with respect to the operation of addition. Obviously inverses do not exist among the rationals with respect to the operation of subtraction since there is no identity element for this operation.

For a system consisting of a set and more than one operation there may be a property connecting any two of its operations.

►**DEFINITION 1.14.** $\begin{Bmatrix} Left \\ Right \end{Bmatrix}$ *Distributivity.* If for any elements a, b, and c in A, $\begin{Bmatrix} a \,②\, (b \,①\, c) = (a \,②\, b) \,①\, (a \,②\, c) \\ (a \,①\, b) \,②\, c = (a \,②\, c) \,①\, (b \,②\, c) \end{Bmatrix}$, then ② is $\begin{Bmatrix} left \\ right \end{Bmatrix}$ *distributive* with respect to ① on A.

In case both operations are commutative on A, either type of distributivity is a consequence of the other, and we say simply that ② is *distributive* with respect to ① on A.

In the set of all integers, multiplication is distributive with respect to addition.

In Exercises 1.11 through 1.15 use the sets and operations of Exercise 1.10.

Exercise 1.11. Discuss the commutativity of the operations on sets 1 through 7.

Exercise 1.12. Discuss the associativity of the operations on sets 1 through 7.

Exercise 1.13. Find all possible identity elements.

Exercise 1.14. Discuss the existence of inverses.

Exercise 1.15. For sets (3) through (6) discuss the distributivity of operation (b) with respect to operation (a).

Exercise 1.16. Are the following operations commutative on the set of integers?

    a. $a \bigcirc b = \min(a,b)$.
    b. $a \bigcirc b = a^2 b$.
    c. $a \bigcirc b = |a + b|$.

Exercise 1.17. If e is an identity element for the operation $\bigcirc$ on the set A, prove that e is unique.

SYSTEMS OF SCALARS

We are now prepared to define the specific mathematical system which will provide the foundation for the ensuing discussion.

▶**DEFINITION 1.15.** A *system $\mathscr{S}$ of scalars* consists of:

A. A set S with at least two elements.
B. The (binary) relation of equality: Two elements are equal if and only if they are the same element.
C. The two operations on S: ① and ②.
D. The nine postulates:

    (1a) ① is commutative.
    (2a) ① is associative.
    (3a) The set S contains an identity element e_0 for ①.
    (4a) With respect to ①, each element in S has an inverse in S.
     (5) ② is distributive with respect to ①.

    (1b) ② is commutative.
    (2b) ② is associative.
    (3b) The set S contains an identity element e_1 for ②.
    (4b) With respect to ②, each element in S except e_0 has an inverse in S.

The elements of the set S in $\mathscr{S}$ are called scalars and will be denoted by lower case italic letters.

Since the operations in the system of scalars will frequently be addition and multiplication, we shall use the standard symbols when the meaning is clear, i.e., the addition and multiplication symbols for ① and ②, respectively, 0 for the additive identity, and 1 for the multiplicative identity.

To illustrate the fact that a system of scalars may be finite, let us consider the system $\mathscr{I}_5$, for which addition and multiplication tables are given in Table 1.1. That both operations are commutative follows from the symmetry of the tables. The associativity of multiplication follows from the definition of multiplication of equivalence classes and the associativity of multiplication on the set of all integers. That is, $\{a\}_5(\{b\}_5\{c\}_5) = \{a\}_5\{bc\}_5 = \{a(bc)\}_5 = \{(ab)c\}_5 = \{ab\}_5\{c\}_5 = (\{a\}_5\{b\}_5)\{c\}_5$. The proofs that addition is associative and that multiplication is distributive with respect to addition follow similarly from the definitions of addition and multiplication of equivalence classes and the corresponding properties of the integers. From Table 1.1 it is readily seen that 0 and 1 are the additive and multiplicative identity elements, respectively. Since there is a 0 in each row and column of the table for addition, each element has an additive inverse. Similarly, the table for multiplication shows that every element except the 0 element has a multiplicative inverse. Thus $\mathscr{I}_5$ is a system of scalars.

Exercise 1.18. Using addition as ①, multiplication as ②, and the results of Exercises 1.11 through 1.15, and taking set S as: (a) all rational numbers, (b) all real numbers, (c) all complex numbers, show that the resulting systems are systems of scalars. (Henceforth these three systems will be denoted by $\mathscr{R}$, $\mathscr{R}^{\#}$, and $\mathscr{C}$, respectively.)

Exercise 1.19. Show that addition is associative and that multiplication distributes with respect to addition in $\mathscr{I}_5$.

Exercise 1.20. Which of $\mathscr{I}_2$, $\mathscr{I}_6$, and $\mathscr{I}_7$ are systems of scalars? Justify your answers.

Exercise 1.21. For what values of m is $\mathscr{I}_m$ a system of scalars?

Exercise 1.22. For any a in a system of scalars show that $ae_0 = e_0$.

CHAPTER II

Vector Spaces

INTRODUCTION

The mathematical system called a *vector space* is made up of two distinct systems and an operation linking them. One of the subsystems is the system of scalars defined in Chapter I. The other subsystem is a system of vectors which will now be developed.

▶**DEFINITION 2.1.** A *vector α of order n over $\mathscr{S}$* is a sequence of n scalars $a_1, a_2, \ldots, a_n$, symbolized by $\alpha = (a_1, a_2, \ldots, a_n)$.

Lower case Greek letters will be used to denote vectors.

▶**DEFINITION 2.2.** *Equality of vectors.* Two vectors $\alpha = (a_1, a_2, \ldots, a_n)$ and $\beta = (b_1, b_2, \ldots, b_n)$ over $\mathscr{S}$ are equal if and only if $a_1 = b_1, a_2 = b_2, \ldots, a_n = b_n$ or, using different notation, if and only if $a_i = b_i$ for $i = 1, 2, \ldots, n$.

▶**DEFINITION 2.3.** *Vector addition.* The *sum* of two vectors α and β of order n over $\mathscr{S}$ is the vector $\alpha \;③\; \beta = (a_1 + b_1, a_2 + b_2, \ldots, a_n + b_n)$.

Because vectors are denoted by Greek letters and scalars by lower-case italic letters, no confusion can arise from using the addition symbol to denote vector addition as well as scalar addition.

▶**THEOREM 2.1.** Vector addition is commutative.

PROOF: From the definition of vector addition and the commutativity of scalar addition, it follows that

$$\alpha + \beta = (a_1 + b_1, a_2 + b_2, \ldots, a_n + b_n)$$
$$= (b_1 + a_1, b_2 + a_2, \ldots, b_n + a_n) = \beta + \alpha$$

▶ **THEOREM 2.2.** Vector addition is associative.

PROOF: Exercise.

▶ **DEFINITION 2.4.** A *system* $\mathscr{V}$ *of vectors* consists of:
A. A set V of vectors of order n over $\mathscr{S}$.
B. The relation of equality of vectors.
C. The operation of vector addition.
D. The two postulates:
  (1) The set V contains an identity element ϵ_0 (the zero vector) for vector addition.
  (2) With respect to vector addition each element in V has an inverse in V.

To illustrate, let $\mathscr{S} = \mathscr{R}$ and let V be the set of all third order vectors (a_1, a_2, a_3) where the a_i are integers. To show that vector addition is an operation on V, it is sufficient to show that the sum of any two vectors in V is a vector in V. But since the sum of two integers is an integer, it follows that in $(c_1, c_2, c_3) = (a_1 + b_1, a_2 + b_2, a_3 + b_3) = (a_1, a_2, a_3) + (b_1, b_2, b_3)$ the c_i are integers; hence (c_1, c_2, c_3) is in V. The vector $(0,0,0)$ is in V and is ϵ_0, since $(0,0,0) + (a_1, a_2, a_3) = (a_1, a_2, a_3) + (0,0,0) = (a_1, a_2, a_3)$. If $\alpha = (a_1, a_2, a_3)$ is in V, then $(-a_1, -a_2, -a_3)$ is also in V and is the inverse of α since $(a_1, a_2, a_3) + (-a_1, -a_2, -a_3) = (-a_1, -a_2, -a_3) + (a_1, a_2, a_3) = \epsilon_0$. Thus the postulates for a vector system are satisfied.

▶ **THEOREM 2.3.** If V is the set of *all* vectors of order n over $\mathscr{S}$, then the corresponding $\mathscr{V}$ is a system of vectors.

PROOF: Exercise.

This particular system of *all* vectors of order n over $\mathscr{S}$ will be denoted by $\mathscr{V}_n$. We now have the two systems necessary for a vector space and need to define the operation connecting them. This operation differs from the previous operations in that it is an operation on two sets, specifically a mapping of the Cartesian product $S \times V$ into V.

▶**DEFINITION 2.5.** *Multiplication of a vector by a scalar.* The *product of a scalar c and a vector* $\alpha = (a_1, a_2, \ldots, a_n)$ is $c\alpha = (ca_1, ca_2, \ldots, ca_n)$.

By Definition 2.5 multiplication of a vector by a scalar is a mapping of $S \times V$ into V'. Extending Definition 1.9, we will call such a mapping an operation if and only if $V' = V$.

▶**DEFINITION 2.6.** The system $\mathscr{V}(\mathscr{S})$ consisting of the system of scalars $\mathscr{S}$ and the system of vectors $\mathscr{V}$ of order n over $\mathscr{S}$ together with the operation of multiplication of a vector by a scalar is a *vector space over* $\mathscr{S}$.

For example, let $\mathscr{S} = \mathscr{R}$ and let $\mathscr{V}$ be the system of third order vectors (a_1, a_2, a_3) with a_1 and a_2 arbitrary rational numbers and $a_3 = 0$. That this is a system of vectors is readily verified. Since multiplication of any vector $(a_1, a_2, 0)$ of V by any scalar c of $\mathscr{R}$ gives the vector $(ca_1, ca_2, 0)$ which is in V, multiplication of a vector by a scalar is an operation. Thus this system $\mathscr{V}(\mathscr{R})$ is a vector space.

If a_1 and a_2 were restricted to integers and again $a_3 = 0$, the resulting $\mathscr{V}$ could readily be verified to be a system of vectors of order three over $\mathscr{R}$. However, multiplication of a vector by a scalar would not be an operation since $1.5(1,2,0) = (1.5,3,0)$ is not in V. Thus not every system of vectors over $\mathscr{S}$ linked to $\mathscr{S}$ by multiplication of a vector by a scalar forms a vector space since the multiplication linking them is not necessarily an operation.

▶**THEOREM 2.4.** $\mathscr{V}_n(\mathscr{S})$ is a vector space.

PROOF: Exercise.

Exercise 2.1. Let V be the set of all vectors of order two over $\mathscr{J}_3$.
   a. List the elements of V.
   b. Show that the corresponding $\mathscr{V}$ is a system of vectors.
   c. Show that the corresponding $\mathscr{V}(\mathscr{J}_3)$ is a vector space.
   d. Is it proper to denote this system by $\mathscr{V}_2(\mathscr{J}_3)$? Justify your answer.

Exercise 2.2. For any $\mathscr{V}(\mathscr{S})$
   a. Show that $\epsilon_0 = (e_0, e_0, \ldots, e_0)$.
   b. Show that $a\epsilon_0 = \epsilon_0$ for any a in $\mathscr{S}$.

Exercise 2.3. For any $\mathscr{S}$ let V contain only the zero vector of order n.
   a. Show that the corresponding $\mathscr{V}$ is a system of vectors.
   b. Show that the corresponding $\mathscr{V}(\mathscr{S})$ is a vector space.

Exercise 2.4. Let $\mathscr{S} = \mathscr{R}^{\#}$ and V be the set of all complex numbers $a + bi$ written as second order vectors (a,b).
   a. Show that the corresponding $\mathscr{V}$ is a system of vectors.
   b. Show that the corresponding $\mathscr{V}(\mathscr{S})$ is a vector space.

Exercise 2.5. Let $\mathscr{S} = \mathscr{R}$ and V be the set of all vectors $(a_1, a_2, a_1 + a_2)$, where a_1 and a_2 are arbitrary rational numbers.
   a. Show that the corresponding $\mathscr{V}$ is a system of vectors.
   b. Show that the corresponding $\mathscr{V}(\mathscr{S})$ is a vector space.

BASIS AND DIMENSION

▶**DEFINITION 2.7.** *Linear dependence.* The set of k vectors $\alpha_1, \alpha_2, \ldots, \alpha_k$ in $\mathscr{V}(\mathscr{S})$ is called *linearly dependent* over $\mathscr{S}$ if and only if there exist k scalars $a_1, a_2, \ldots, a_k$ (not all zero) in S such that $a_1\alpha_1 + a_2\alpha_2 + \ldots + a_k\alpha_k = \sum_{i=1}^{k} a_i\alpha_i \equiv \epsilon_0$.

▶**DEFINITION 2.8.** *Linear independence.* Any set of vectors which is not linearly dependent over $\mathscr{S}$ is said to be *linearly independent* over $\mathscr{S}$.

For example, the set of three vectors $(1,2)$, $(0,-1)$, and $(2,3)$ is linearly dependent over $\mathscr{R}$ since $2(1,2) + (0,-1) + (-1)(2,3) = (0,0)$. However, the set of two vectors $(0,1)$ and $(1,0)$ is linearly independent over the same system since $a(0,1) + b(1,0) = (b,a)$, which is $(0,0)$ if and only if $a = b = 0$.

The determination of the linear dependence or independence of a set of k vectors of order n leads to a homogeneous system of n linear equations in k unknowns. Although for small n the solution of such a system of equations is relatively simple, a general method of solution will be discussed in Chapter V.

▶**THEOREM 2.5.** Any set of vectors in $\mathscr{V}(\mathscr{S})$ which contains the zero vector is necessarily linearly dependent over $\mathscr{S}$.

PROOF: Exercise.

▶**DEFINITION 2.9.** In $\mathscr{V}(\mathscr{S})$ a vector $\beta = \sum\limits_{i=1}^{k} a_i \alpha_i$ is called a *linear combination* of the vectors α_i $(i = 1,2, \ldots ,k)$.

For example, in $\mathscr{V}_3(\mathscr{R})$ the vector $(2,4,2)$ is a linear combination of $(1,1,2)$, $(0,-1,1)$, and $(2,0,-1)$ since $(2,4,2) = 2(1,1,2) + (-2)(0,-1,1) + 0(2,0,-1)$.

▶**THEOREM 2.6.** Let α_i $(i = 1,2, \ldots ,k)$ be vectors of order n over $\mathscr{S}$ and V be the set of all linear combinations of these k vectors. The corresponding $\mathscr{V}(\mathscr{S})$ is a vector space.

PROOF: First it will be shown that the corresponding $\mathscr{V}$ is a system of vectors. This requires that vector addition be an operation, that V contain the zero vector, and that each vector in V have an inverse in V. Since the sum

$$\beta_1 + \beta_2 = \sum_{i=1}^{k} a_i \alpha_i + \sum_{i=1}^{k} b_i \alpha_i = \sum_{i=1}^{k} (a_i + b_i)\alpha_i = \sum_{i=1}^{k} c_i \alpha_i = \beta_3$$

is in V, vector addition is an operation. Now $\epsilon_0 = \sum\limits_{i=1}^{k} e_0 \alpha_i$; hence V contains the zero vector. Denoting the additive inverse of a in $\mathscr{S}$ by $-a$, for any vector $\beta_1 = \sum\limits_{i=1}^{k} a_i\alpha_i$ in V there is a corresponding inverse $\beta_2 = \sum\limits_{i=1}^{k} (-a_i)\alpha_i$ in V.

Finally, to show that the corresponding $\mathscr{V}(\mathscr{S})$ is a vector space requires that multiplication of a vector by a scalar be an operation. This is shown by the fact that

$$c\beta = c \sum_{i=1}^{k} a_i\alpha_i = \sum_{i=1}^{k} (ca_i)\alpha_i = \sum_{i=1}^{k} d_i\alpha_i$$

is in V, thus proving the theorem.

▶**DEFINITION 2.10.** Any set of vectors α_i $(i = 1, 2, \ldots, k)$ of order n over $\mathscr{S}$ is said to *generate the vector space* $\mathscr{V}(\mathscr{S})$ if the corresponding V is the set of all linear combinations of the α_i.

▶**DEFINITION 2.11.** A vector $\alpha = (a_1, a_2, \ldots, a_n)$ over $\mathscr{S}$ is a *unit vector* if and only if $\sum\limits_{i=1}^{n} a_i^2 = e_1$ in $\mathscr{S}$.

For example, in $\mathscr{V}_3(\mathscr{R}^{\#})$ some of the unit vectors are $(1/2, 1/2, \sqrt{2}/2)$, $(0, 1, 0)$, $(1/2, 0, \sqrt{3}/2)$, and $(1/3, 2/3, 2/3)$. In $\mathscr{V}_3(\mathscr{J}_2)$ there are four unit vectors: $(1, 1, 1)$, $(0, 0, 1)$, $(0, 1, 0)$, and $(1, 0, 0)$. In $\mathscr{V}_n(\mathscr{S})$ there exist n unit vectors of a particular form, namely, $\epsilon_i = (a_1, a_2, \ldots, a_n)$ for $i = 1, 2, \ldots, n$ with $a_j = e_0$ for $j \neq i$ and $a_i = e_1$.

▶**THEOREM 2.7.** The vectors ϵ_i $(i = 1, 2, \ldots, n)$ in $\mathscr{V}_n(\mathscr{S})$ are linearly independent over $\mathscr{S}$.

PROOF: Exercise.

▶**THEOREM 2.8.** $\mathscr{V}_n(\mathscr{S})$ is generated by the ϵ_i $(i = 1, 2, \ldots, n)$.

PROOF: Let $\alpha = (a_1, a_2, \ldots, a_n)$ be any vector in $\mathscr{V}_n(\mathscr{S})$; then $\alpha = \sum\limits_{i=1}^{n} a_i\epsilon_i$.

▶ COROLLARY. Each vector in $\mathscr{V}_n(\mathscr{S})$ is a linear combination of the ϵ_i $(i = 1, 2, \ldots, n)$ in $\mathscr{V}_n(\mathscr{S})$.

▶ DEFINITION 2.12. A set of k linearly independent vectors in $\mathscr{V}(\mathscr{S})$ is said to constitute a *basis* of $\mathscr{V}(\mathscr{S})$ if and only if the k vectors generate $\mathscr{V}(\mathscr{S})$.

▶ THEOREM 2.9. The vectors ϵ_i $(i = 1, 2, \ldots, n)$ in $\mathscr{V}_n(\mathscr{S})$ constitute a basis of $\mathscr{V}_n(\mathscr{S})$.

PROOF: The theorem follows from Theorem 2.7 and Theorem 2.8.

▶ THEOREM 2.10. If one basis of a vector space consists of k vectors, then every basis of that space consists of k vectors.

PROOF: Let $\alpha_1, \alpha_2, \ldots, \alpha_k$ and $\beta_1, \beta_2, \ldots, \beta_r$ be two bases of $\mathscr{V}(\mathscr{S})$ with $r \geq k$. Since β_1 belongs to $\mathscr{V}(\mathscr{S})$, we have $\beta_1 = \sum_{i=1}^{k} a_{1i}\alpha_i$ with some $a_{1i} \neq e_0$. (For otherwise $\beta_1 = \epsilon_0$, contrary to Theorem 2.5.) If necessary, renumber so that $a_{11} \neq e_0$. Denoting the multiplicative inverse of a by a^{-1} in $\mathscr{S}$, we then have $\alpha_1 = a_{11}^{-1}(\beta_1 - \sum_{i=2}^{k} a_{1i}\alpha_i)$ so that any vector in $\mathscr{V}(\mathscr{S})$ can be represented as a linear combination of $\beta_1, \alpha_2, \alpha_3, \ldots, \alpha_k$. To show that this set is linearly independent, assume that $c_1\beta_1 + c_2\alpha_2 + \ldots + c_k\alpha_k = \epsilon_0$ with some $c_i \neq e_0$. If c_1 were e_0, then $\alpha_2, \alpha_3, \ldots, \alpha_k$ would be linearly dependent; hence $c_1 \neq e_0$. Substituting $\beta_1 = \sum_{i=1}^{k} a_{1i}\alpha_i$, we have $c_1 a_{11}\alpha_1 + \sum_{i=2}^{k}(c_1 a_{1i} + c_i)\alpha_i = \epsilon_0$ with $c_1 a_{11} \neq e_0$ contrary to the linear independence of the $\alpha_1, \ldots, \alpha_k$. Thus $\beta_1, \alpha_2, \ldots, \alpha_k$ constitute a basis of $\mathscr{V}(\mathscr{S})$. Then $\beta_2 = a_{21}\beta_1 + \sum_{i=2}^{k} a_{2i}\alpha_i$, and by a similar argument we show that $\beta_1, \beta_2, \alpha_3, \ldots, \alpha_k$ constitute a basis. Applying this procedure j times, $1 \leq j < k$, we have $\beta_1, \beta_2, \ldots, \beta_j, \alpha_{j+1}, \ldots, \alpha_k$

as a basis for $\mathscr{V}(\mathscr{S})$. Then $\beta_{j+1} = \sum\limits_{i=1}^{j} a_{(j+1)i}\beta_i + \sum\limits_{i=j+1}^{k} a_{(j+1)i}\alpha_i$
with some $a_{(j+1)i} \neq e_0$ for $i = (j+1), \ldots, k$. For if all
$a_{(j+1)i} = e_0$ for $i = (j+1), \ldots, k$, then the $\beta_1, \beta_2, \ldots, \beta_{j+1}$
would be linearly dependent contrary to the original assumption.

Assuming (renumbering if necessary) $a_{(j+1)(j+1)} \neq e_0$, then

$$\alpha_{j+1} = a_{(j+1)(j+1)}^{-1}(\beta_{j+1} - \sum\limits_{i=1}^{j} a_{(j+1)i}\beta_i - \sum\limits_{i=j+2}^{k} a_{(j+1)i}\alpha_i)$$

and, as above, we can show that $\beta_1, \beta_2, \ldots, \beta_{j+1}, \alpha_{j+2}, \ldots, \alpha_k$
constitute a basis of $\mathscr{V}(\mathscr{S})$. After k applications of this argument we have $\beta_1, \beta_2, \ldots, \beta_k$ as a basis for $\mathscr{V}(\mathscr{S})$. Now if
$r > k$, then $\beta_{k+1} = \sum\limits_{i=1}^{k} b_i\beta_i$, and the set of r vectors β_i would be
linearly dependent and could not be a basis. Hence $r = k$.

▶**THEOREM 2.11.** If a set of vectors generates $\mathscr{V}(\mathscr{S})$, then
the set contains a basis of $\mathscr{V}(\mathscr{S})$.

PROOF: Exercise.

▶**DEFINITION 2.13.** The *dimension* of a vector space $\mathscr{V}(\mathscr{S})$
is the number of vectors in any basis of the space and is denoted
by $d[\mathscr{V}(\mathscr{S})]$.

Since the ϵ_i $(i = 1,2, \ldots, n)$ constitute a basis for $\mathscr{V}_n(\mathscr{S})$, we
have $d[\mathscr{V}_n(\mathscr{S})] = n$.

Exercise 2.6. In $\mathscr{V}_2(\mathscr{J}_3)$
   a. List all unit vectors.
   b. List all bases consisting only of unit vectors.

Exercise 2.7. For the vector space in Exercise 2.5
   a. Find $d[\mathscr{V}(\mathscr{S})]$.
   b. Find a basis for $\mathscr{V}(\mathscr{S})$, the components of whose vectors are
0's and 1's.
   c. Find another basis for $\mathscr{V}(\mathscr{S})$, none of whose vectors have 0
components.

Exercise 2.8. Consider the vector space $\mathscr{V}(\mathscr{R})$ generated by the four vectors $\alpha_1 = (1,2,3)$, $\alpha_2 = (-1,0,2)$, $\alpha_3 = (2,2,1)$, and $\alpha_4 = (0,2,5)$.

  a. What is its dimension?
  b. Give a basis not containing any of the α_i.
  c. Does this vector space contain any of the ϵ_i $(i = 1,2,3)$?

SUBSPACE OF A VECTOR SPACE

▶**DEFINITION 2.14.** If $\mathscr{U}(\mathscr{S})$ and $\mathscr{V}(\mathscr{S})$ are each vector spaces over $\mathscr{S}$ such that every vector in $\mathscr{U}(\mathscr{S})$ is also in $\mathscr{V}(\mathscr{S})$, then $\mathscr{U}(\mathscr{S})$ is a *subspace* of $\mathscr{V}(\mathscr{S})$.

It might be pointed out that under this definition the space consisting of the zero vector of order n alone is a subspace of $\mathscr{V}_n(\mathscr{S})$ and that every vector space is a subspace of itself. That the zero vector alone constitutes a vector space was proved in Exercise 2.3.

For example, the space of all vectors $(a,b,0)$ with a,b in $\mathscr{S}$ is a subspace of $\mathscr{V}_3(\mathscr{S})$.

▶**THEOREM 2.12.** If $\mathscr{U}(\mathscr{S})$ is a subspace of $\mathscr{V}(\mathscr{S})$, then $d[\mathscr{U}(\mathscr{S})] \leq d[\mathscr{V}(\mathscr{S})]$.

PROOF: Since both $\mathscr{U}(\mathscr{S})$ and $\mathscr{V}(\mathscr{S})$ are vector spaces over the same system of scalars $\mathscr{S}$, any set of vectors in $\mathscr{U}(\mathscr{S})$ which is linearly independent over $\mathscr{S}$ is also a set of vectors in $\mathscr{V}(\mathscr{S})$ which is linearly independent over $\mathscr{S}$. Thus any basis of $\mathscr{U}(\mathscr{S})$ is a set of vectors in $\mathscr{V}(\mathscr{S})$ which is linearly independent over $\mathscr{S}$. Hence any basis of $\mathscr{V}(\mathscr{S})$ must contain at least as many vectors as a basis of $\mathscr{U}(\mathscr{S})$.

▶**THEOREM 2.13.** A set of vectors α_i $(i = 1,2,\ldots,k)$ in $\mathscr{V}(\mathscr{S})$, containing at most r vectors linearly independent over $\mathscr{S}$, generates a subspace $\mathscr{U}(\mathscr{S})$ of dimension r.

PROOF: That $\mathscr{U}(\mathscr{S})$ is a subspace of $\mathscr{V}(\mathscr{S})$ is obvious. Without loss of generality, assume that $\alpha_1, \alpha_2, \ldots, \alpha_r$ are linearly independent over $\mathscr{S}$. Let $\beta = \alpha_j \, (j = r + 1, \ldots, k)$. Since the set of vectors $\alpha_1, \alpha_2, \ldots, a_r, \beta$ is linearly dependent over $\mathscr{S}$, there exist scalars such that $\sum_{i=1}^{r} a_i\alpha_i + b\beta = \epsilon_0$ with $b \neq e_0$. (For if $b = e_0$, then $\sum_{i=1}^{r} a_i\alpha_i = \epsilon_0$ with some $a_i \neq e_0$ contrary to the linear independence of the $\alpha_i \, (i = 1,2,\ldots,r)$.) Hence $\beta = -b^{-1}\sum_{i=1}^{r} a_i\alpha_i$; that is, $\alpha_{r+1}, \ldots, \alpha_k$ are linear combinations of $\alpha_1, \alpha_2, \ldots, \alpha_r$. Thus the $\alpha_i \, (i = 1,2,\ldots,r)$ constitute a basis of $\mathscr{U}(\mathscr{S})$, and we have $d[\mathscr{U}(\mathscr{S})] = r$.

▶**COROLLARY.** Any set of linear combinations of the $\alpha_i \, (i = 1,2,\ldots,k)$ contains at most r vectors linearly independent over $\mathscr{S}$.

SCALAR PRODUCT AND ORTHOGONALITY

We now define another operation on the two sets in $\mathscr{V}(\mathscr{S})$, specifically a mapping of $V \times V$ into S.

▶**DEFINITION 2.15.** In $\mathscr{V}(\mathscr{S})$ the *scalar product* of two vectors α and β is the scalar c defined by $c = \alpha \cdot \beta = (a_1, a_2, \ldots, a_n)(b_1, b_2, \ldots, b_n) = a_1b_1 + a_2b_2 + \ldots + a_nb_n = \sum_{i=1}^{n} a_ib_i$.

▶**DEFINITION 2.16.** *Orthogonality.* Two vectors α and β in $\mathscr{V}(\mathscr{S})$, where $\mathscr{S}$ is a subsystem of $\mathscr{R}^{\#}$, are *orthogonal* to each other if and only if $\alpha \cdot \beta = 0$.

By this definition the vector ϵ_0 is orthogonal to all vectors in $\mathscr{V}(\mathscr{R}^{\#})$, including itself. No other vector in $\mathscr{V}(\mathscr{R}^{\#})$ is orthogonal to itself. It was to assure this property that we restricted the definition to subsystems of $\mathscr{R}^{\#}$. Without this restriction we might have had nonzero vectors orthogonal to themselves. Examples of such include $(1,1,0)$ in $\mathscr{V}_3(\mathscr{J}_2)$ and $(1,i)$ in $\mathscr{V}_2(\mathscr{C})$.

▶**THEOREM 2.14.** If a vector α is orthogonal to each of the vectors α_1, α_2, ..., α_k, then α is orthogonal to every vector in the space $\mathscr{V}(\mathscr{S})$ generated by the α_i ($i = 1,2, \ldots, k$).

PROOF: Since in $\mathscr{V}(\mathscr{S})$ any vector $\beta = \sum_{i=1}^{k} b_i \alpha_i$, we have $\alpha \cdot \beta = \sum_{i=1}^{k} b_i (\alpha \cdot \alpha_i) = 0.$

▶**THEOREM 2.15.** Any set of mutually orthogonal nonzero vectors in $\mathscr{V}(\mathscr{S})$ is linearly independent over $\mathscr{S}$.

PROOF: Let α_1, α_2, ..., α_k be a set of mutually orthogonal nonzero vectors. If these vectors were linearly dependent over $\mathscr{S}$, there would exist c_i's (not all zero) such that $\sum_{i=1}^{k} c_i \alpha_i = \epsilon_0$. Assume $c_j \neq 0$. Then $\alpha_j \cdot \sum_{i=1}^{k} c_i \alpha_i = \sum_{i=1}^{k} c_i (\alpha_j \cdot \alpha_i) = c_j (\alpha_j \cdot \alpha_j) = 0$, which is a contradiction. Hence the vectors are linearly independent.

▶**THEOREM 2.16.** Every vector space $\mathscr{V}(\mathscr{S})$ of dimension k contains a set of exactly k mutually orthogonal nonzero vectors.

PROOF: Let α_1, α_2, ..., α_k be a basis of $\mathscr{V}(\mathscr{S})$. Let $\beta_1 = \alpha_1$ and let

$$\beta_2 = \alpha_2 - \left[\frac{\alpha_2 \cdot \beta_1}{\beta_1 \cdot \beta_1} \right] \beta_1; \quad \beta_3 = \alpha_3 - \left[\frac{\alpha_3 \cdot \beta_2}{\beta_2 \cdot \beta_2} \right] \beta_2$$

$$- \left[\frac{\alpha_3 \cdot \beta_1}{\beta_1 \cdot \beta_1} \right] \beta_1; \ldots; \quad \beta_k = \alpha_k - \sum_{i=1}^{k-1} \left[\frac{\alpha_k \cdot \beta_i}{\beta_i \cdot \beta_i} \right] \beta_i$$

The verification that the β_i's are mutually orthogonal is left as an exercise. Since $\beta_j = \sum_{i=1}^{j} a_i \alpha_i$ with $a_j \neq 0$, we have every $\beta_j \neq \epsilon_0$, for otherwise the α_i would be linearly dependent. By Theorem 2.15 the β_i's are linearly independent over $\mathscr{S}$, and hence they form a basis of $\mathscr{V}(\mathscr{S})$. Thus any vector γ in $\mathscr{V}(\mathscr{S})$ is a linear combination of the β_i's, $\gamma = \sum\limits_{i=1}^{k} c_i \beta_i$. If $c_j \neq 0$, we have $\beta_j \cdot \gamma = \sum\limits_{i=1}^{k} c_i \beta_j \cdot \beta_i = c_j \beta_j \cdot \beta_j \neq 0$. Hence no other non-zero vector in $\mathscr{V}(\mathscr{S})$ can be orthogonal to all of the β_i's.

Exercise 2.9. Show that the scalar product of any unit vector with itself is e_1.

Exercise 2.10. Show that in $\mathscr{V}_n(\mathscr{R}^{\#})$ the vectors ϵ_i ($i = 1, 2, \ldots, n$) form a mutually orthogonal basis.

Exercise 2.11. Using the procedure of the proof of Theorem 2.16, construct a basis of mutually orthogonal vectors for $\mathscr{V}_3(\mathscr{R})$ from the basis $\alpha_1 = (1,1,0)$, $\alpha_2 = (1,0,1)$, and $\alpha_3 = (0,1,1)$.

Exercise 2.12. Are $(1,2,3)$ and $(3,2,1)$ unit vectors and/or orthogonal when considered as vectors in $\mathscr{V}_3(\mathscr{J}_5)$? In $\mathscr{V}_3(\mathscr{J}_{13})$? In $\mathscr{V}_3(\mathscr{R})$?

CHAPTER III

Linear Transformations

IMAGES AND IMAGE SPACES

In the previous chapters mappings of one set into another were discussed. In particular, operations were defined as such mappings. We now wish to consider mappings of one system into another, specifically one vector space into another. This means that we must be concerned with the operations as well as with the elements of the sets. We shall define a particular type of mapping which preserves operations.

▶**DEFINITION 3.1.** A *linear transformation* T of $\mathscr{V}(\mathscr{F})$ into $\mathscr{U}(\mathscr{F})$ is a mapping T of V onto V', a subset of U, satisfying the following conditions:

(1) If $\alpha T = \alpha'$, then $(a\alpha)T = a\alpha'$.
(2) If $\alpha_1 T = \alpha_1'$ and $\alpha_2 T = \alpha_2'$, then $(\alpha_1 + \alpha_2)T = \alpha_1' + \alpha_2'$.

The α' into which α maps under the linear transformation will be called the *image* of α. As in all mappings the image α' is uniquely determined by α, but α is not necessarily uniquely determined by α'.

Conditions (1) and (2) of Definition 3.1 stated in words specify respectively that multiplication of a vector by a scalar and vector addition are preserved. As a mnemonic device these conditions may be loosely rephrased as: the image of a scalar multiple is the scalar multiple of the image, and the image of a sum is the sum of the images.

As an example of a linear transformation, let the image of $\alpha = (a,b,c)$ in $\mathscr{V}_3(\mathscr{R})$ be $\alpha T = \alpha' = (a + b, 2c)$ in $\mathscr{V}_2(\mathscr{R})$. Condition (1) is satisfied since $(k\alpha)T = (ka,kb,kc)T = (ka + kb, 2kc) = k\alpha'$. To show that condition (2) is satisfied, let

$\alpha_1 = (a_1,b_1,c_1)$ and $\alpha_2 = (a_2,b_2,c_2)$. Then $(\alpha_1 + \alpha_2)T = (a_1 + a_2,$ $b_1 + b_2,\ c_1 + c_2)T = (a_1 + a_2 + b_1 + b_2,\ 2c_1 + 2c_2) = (a_1 + b_1,\ 2c_1) + (a_2 + b_2,\ 2c_2) = \alpha_1' + \alpha_2'$. Note that the images are not distinct since, for example, $(1,2,3)T = (2,1,3)T = (3,6)$.

As an example of a mapping which is not a linear transformation, let the image of $\alpha = (a,b,c)$ in $\mathscr{V}_3(\mathscr{R})$ be $\alpha T = \alpha' = (a + 2,b,c)$ in $\mathscr{V}_3(\mathscr{R})$. This does not satisfy condition (1) since $k\alpha T = (ka,kb,kc)T = (ka + 2,kb,kc)$, whereas $k\alpha' = (ka + 2k,kb,kc)$.

As a second example of a linear transformation, let the image of $\alpha = (a,b,c)$ in $\mathscr{V}_3(\mathscr{R})$ be $\alpha T = \alpha' = (b + c, a + c, a + b)$ in $\mathscr{V}_3(\mathscr{R})$. Condition (1) is satisfied since $(k\alpha)T = (ka,kb,kc)T = (kb + kc, ka + kc, ka + kb) = k(b + c, a + c, a + b) = k\alpha'$. Condition (2) is satisfied since $(\alpha_1 + \alpha_2)T = (a_1 + a_2, b_1 + b_2, c_1 + c_2)T = (b_1 + b_2 + c_1 + c_2, a_1 + a_2 + c_1 + c_2, a_1 + a_2 + b_1 + b_2) = (b_1 + c_1,\ a_1 + c_1,\ a_1 + b_1) + (b_2 + c_2,\ a_2 + c_2,\ a_2 + b_2) = \alpha_1' + \alpha_2'$.

▶**THEOREM 3.1.** The *image space* $\mathscr{V}'(\mathscr{S})$ corresponding to the V' of Definition 3.1 is a vector space.

PROOF: Let α and β be vectors in $\mathscr{V}(\mathscr{S})$ with images α' and β' in $\mathscr{V}'(\mathscr{S})$. To prove the theorem we must show that $\alpha' + \beta'$ and $k\alpha'$ are in V'. But since $\mathscr{V}(\mathscr{S})$ is a vector space, it must contain $\alpha + \beta$ and $k\alpha$. Hence, by the definition of a linear transformation, $\alpha' + \beta'$ and $k\alpha'$ are in V'.

▶**THEOREM 3.2.** The images of a basis of a vector space under a linear transformation generate the image space.

PROOF: Exercise. (*Hint:* Any vector in a vector space is a linear combination of the vectors of the basis.)

▶**THEOREM 3.3.** If α_i and β_i ($i = 1,2, \ldots ,n$) are two bases of the same vector space, then the mapping defined by $\gamma T = \left(\sum_{i=1}^{n} a_i\alpha_i \right) T = \sum_{i=1}^{n} a_i\beta_i = \gamma'$ is a linear transformation.

PROOF:

1. $$(k\gamma)T = \left(\sum_{i=1}^{n} ka_i\alpha_i\right) T = \sum_{i=1}^{n} ka_i\beta_i = k\gamma'$$

2. $$(\gamma_1 + \gamma_2)T = \left(\sum_{i=1}^{n} a_i\alpha_i + \sum_{i=1}^{n} b_i\alpha_i\right) T = \left(\sum_{i=1}^{n} (a_i + b_i)\alpha_i\right) T$$

    $$= \sum_{i=1}^{n} (a_i + b_i)\beta_i = \sum_{i=1}^{n} a_i\beta_i + \sum_{i=1}^{n} b_i\beta_i$$

    $$= \gamma_1' + \gamma_2'$$

In Theorem 3.3 $\alpha_i T = \beta_i (i = 1, 2, \ldots, n)$. Thus this type of linear transformation is frequently referred to as a *change of basis*.

Exercise 3.1. Let the image of $\alpha = (a,b)$ in $\mathcal{V}_2(\mathcal{R})$ be $\alpha T = \alpha' = (a + b, b - 1)$ in $\mathcal{V}_2(\mathcal{R})$. Are conditions 1 and 2 of Definition 3.1 satisfied?

Exercise 3.2. With $\alpha = (a,b)$, which of the following are linear transformations of $\mathcal{V}_2(\mathcal{R})$ into $\mathcal{V}_2(\mathcal{R})$?

    a. $\alpha' = (-a,-b)$.

    b. $\alpha' = (b,2a)$.

    c. $\alpha' = (a^2/b,b)$.

    d. $\alpha' = (0,a)$.

    e. $\alpha' = (a,1)$.

    f. $\alpha' = (a - b, a + 2b)$.

Exercise 3.3. Show that conditions (1) and (2) of Definition 3.1 are equivalent to the single condition: If $\alpha_1 T = \alpha_1'$ and $\alpha_2 T = \alpha_2'$, then $(a_1\alpha_1 + a_2\alpha_2)T = a_1\alpha_1' + a_2\alpha_2'$.

NONSINGULAR TRANSFORMATIONS

▶**DEFINITION 3.2.** A linear transformation on $\mathcal{V}(\mathcal{S})$ is *nonsingular* if $d[\mathcal{V}'(\mathcal{S})] = d[\mathcal{V}(\mathcal{S})]$. Otherwise the linear transformation is *singular*.

The linear transformation given as the first example under Definition 3.1 is obviously singular since it maps $\mathcal{V}_3(\mathcal{R})$ into a space whose dimension is at most two. On the other hand, the linear transformation of the other example is nonsingular. Since the vectors $(-1/2, 1/2, 1/2)$, $(1/2, -1/2, 1/2)$, $(1/2, 1/2, -1/2)$ in $\mathscr{V}_3(\mathscr{R})$ map into ϵ_1, ϵ_2, and ϵ_3, respectively, the dimension of the image space is three.

▶**THEOREM 3.4.** Under a nonsingular linear transformation the images of any basis of a vector space constitute a basis of the image space.

PROOF: The theorem follows directly from Theorem 3.2 and Definition 3.2.

▶**THEOREM 3.5.** A linear transformation is uniquely determined by the images of any basis.

PROOF: Exercise.

The images under a linear transformation T_1 of any basis of $\mathscr{V}(\mathscr{S})$ generate $\mathscr{V}'(\mathscr{S})$ by Theorem 3.2. This set of images contains a basis of $\mathscr{V}'(\mathscr{S})$ by Theorem 2.11. The images of this basis under a second linear transformation T_2 generate $\mathscr{V}''(\mathscr{S})$ and contain a basis of $\mathscr{V}''(\mathscr{S})$ by the same theorems. The images in $\mathscr{V}''(\mathscr{S})$ of a basis of $\mathscr{V}(\mathscr{S})$ determine a linear transformation T by Theorem 3.5. Thus we make the following definition.

▶**DEFINITION 3.3.** The single linear transformation T which is equivalent to the transformation T_1 followed by the transformation T_2 is called the *product* T_1T_2.

To illustrate: If T_1 is the linear transformation of the second example in the previous section and T_2 is that of the first example, that is, $\alpha T_1 = (b + c, a + c, a + b)$ and $\alpha T_2 = (a + b, 2c)$, then T_1T_2 maps $\alpha = (a,b,c)$ of $\mathscr{V}_3(\mathscr{R})$ into $\alpha T_1T_2 = \alpha' = (a + b + 2c, 2a + 2b)$. However, the product T_2T_1 does not exist since the image space of T_2 is $\mathscr{V}_2(\mathscr{R})$ while T_1 is not a linear transformation on $\mathscr{V}_2(\mathscr{R})$.

Exercise 3.4. Is change of basis a nonsingular transformation?

Exercise 3.5. Which of the linear transformations in Exercise 3.2 are nonsingular?

Exercise 3.6. Let T_1 and T_2 be defined by $(a,b,c)T_1 = (a + b,c,b)$ and $(a,b,c)T_2 = (b,a,b + c)$.

    a. Show that T_1 and T_2 are nonsingular linear transformations.

    b. Find $(a,b,c)T_1T_2$ and $(a,b,c)T_2T_1$.

    c. Find the dimension of each of the four image spaces.

Exercise 3.7. Let T_1 and T_2 be defined by $(a,b,c)T_1 = (a + b,b,a)$ and $(a,b,c)T_2 = (a - b,c,c)$.

    a. Show that T_1 and T_2 are singular.

    b. Find $(a,b,c)T_1T_2$ and $(a,b,c)T_2T_1$.

    c. Find the dimension of each of the four image spaces.

CHAPTER IV

Matrices

THE VECTOR SPACE OF MATRICES

Let us consider a nonsingular linear transformation of $\mathscr{V}_3(\mathscr{S})$ to $\mathscr{V}_3(\mathscr{S})$. This transforms one basis ξ_i, $(i = 1,2,3)$, into a new basis η_i, $(i = 1,2,3)$. Since the ξ_i's are vectors in $\mathscr{V}_3(\mathscr{S})$, they can be expressed as linear combinations of the η_i's explicitly:

$$\xi_1 = a_{11}\eta_1 + a_{12}\eta_2 + a_{13}\eta_3$$
$$\xi_2 = a_{21}\eta_1 + a_{22}\eta_2 + a_{23}\eta_3 \tag{1}$$
$$\xi_3 = a_{31}\eta_1 + a_{32}\eta_2 + a_{33}\eta_3$$

Since any vector α in $\mathscr{V}_3(\mathscr{S})$ is a linear combination of the ξ_i's, equations (1) enable us to express α as a linear combination of the η_i's. Hence the linear transformation is completely determined by equations (1). However, because the positions of the ξ_i's and η_i's are obvious, equations (1) are determined by the a_{ij}'s. Thus, to determine the linear transformation, we need only the three-by-three array:

$$
\begin{array}{ccc}
a_{11} & a_{12} & a_{13} \\
a_{21} & a_{22} & a_{23} \\
a_{31} & a_{32} & a_{33}
\end{array}
$$

To take advantage of this abbreviated form, we define:

▶DEFINITION 4.1. An $m \times n$ *matrix* over $\mathscr{S}$ is a rectangular array of scalars from S consisting of m rows and n

columns of the form

$$\begin{pmatrix} a_{11} & a_{12} & a_{13} & \cdots & a_{1n} \\ a_{21} & a_{22} & a_{23} & \cdots & a_{2n} \\ \cdot & & & & \cdot \\ \cdot & & & & \cdot \\ \cdot & & & & \cdot \\ a_{m1} & a_{m2} & a_{m3} & \cdots & a_{mn} \end{pmatrix}$$

We may abbreviate this further by writing $_m(a_{ij})_n$ rather than by writing the entire array, and if the number of rows and columns can be established readily from the context, we may write simply (a_{ij}). We shall employ capital roman letters to represent matrices, i.e., $_mA_n = {}_m(a_{ij})_n$, or simply $B = (b_{ij})$.

Since each row or column of a matrix is a sequence of scalars, we make the following definition.

▶DEFINITION 4.2. The vector $\alpha_{ri} \equiv (a_{i1}, a_{i2}, \ldots, a_{in})$, the ith row of the matrix $_m(a_{ij})_n$. Similarly, the vector $\alpha_{cj} \equiv (a_{1j}, a_{2j}, \ldots, a_{mj})$, the jth column of the matrix $_m(a_{ij})_n$.

▶DEFINITION 4.3. *Equality of matrices.* Two matrices over $\mathscr{S}$ are equal if and only if corresponding elements are identical, i.e., $A = B$ if and only if $a_{ij} = b_{ij}$ ($i = 1, 2, \ldots, m$; $i = 1, 2, \ldots, n$) in S.

▶DEFINITION 4.4. *Matrix addition.* The *sum of matrices* over $\mathscr{S}$, $A = {}_m(a_{ij})_n$ and $B = {}_m(b_{ij})_n$, is the matrix $C = A + B = {}_m(a_{ij} + b_{ij})_n$ in S.

The sum of the matrices $_mA_n$ and $_pQ_q$ is undefined unless both $m = p$ and $n = q$. For example, over $\mathscr{R}$

$$\begin{pmatrix} 0 & 1 \\ -2 & 1 \\ 7 & 7 \end{pmatrix} + \begin{pmatrix} 4 & 1 \\ 0 & 9 \\ 2 & -3 \end{pmatrix} = \begin{pmatrix} 4 & 2 \\ -2 & 10 \\ 9 & 4 \end{pmatrix}$$

▶**THEOREM 4.1.** Matrix addition is commutative and associative.

PROOF: If the m rows of the $m \times n$ matrix over $\mathscr{S}$, (a_{ij}), were rewritten sequentially as a single row, the matrix would appear as $(a_{11}, a_{12}, \ldots, a_{1n}, a_{21}, \ldots, a_{2n}, a_{31}, \ldots, a_{mn})$. In this form the matrix could be considered as a vector of order mn over $\mathscr{S}$. Thus there is a one-to-one correspondence between the set of all $m \times n$ matrices over $\mathscr{S}$ and the set of all vectors of order mn over $\mathscr{S}$. Furthermore, the sum of two matrices corresponds to the sum of the corresponding vectors. Thus the theorem is a direct consequence of Theorems 2.1 and 2.2.

▶**COROLLARY.** The system consisting of all $m \times n$ matrices over $\mathscr{S}$, equality of matrices, and matrix addition is a system of vectors.

This corollary follows directly from the one-to-one correspondence between the matrices and vectors and Theorem 2.3. The ϵ_0 of this system of vectors corresponds to the $m \times n$ matrix, all of whose elements are e_0. This matrix is called the *zero matrix* and will be denoted by $_mZ_n$ or simply by Z.

To make this system of vectors into a vector space requires a definition for the operation of multiplication by a scalar.

▶**DEFINITION 4.5.** *Multiplication of a matrix by a scalar.* The product of $_mA_n = {}_m(a_{ij})_n$, a matrix over $\mathscr{S}$, by a scalar c in S is the matrix $c \, _mA_n = {}_m(ca_{ij})_n$.

Since with this definition the scalar multiple of a matrix corresponds to the scalar multiple of the corresponding vector, the following theorem is a consequence of Theorem 2.4.

▶**THEOREM 4.2.** The system consisting of the system of scalars $\mathscr{S}$ and the vector system of all $m \times n$ matrices over $\mathscr{S}$, together with the operation of multiplication of a matrix by a scalar, is a vector space of dimension mn over $\mathscr{S}$.

Exercise 4.1. Perform the indicated operations for the following matrices over $\mathscr{R}$.

a. $\begin{pmatrix} 1 & 2 & 3 \\ 4 & 5 & 6 \end{pmatrix} + \begin{pmatrix} 3 & 7 & 8 \\ 9 & -1 & 7 \end{pmatrix} =$

b. $\begin{pmatrix} 1 & 2 & 3 \\ 4 & 5 & 6 \end{pmatrix} + \begin{pmatrix} 4 & -5 & 6 \\ -2 & 3 & -5 \end{pmatrix} + \begin{pmatrix} -5 & 3 & -9 \\ -2 & -8 & -1 \end{pmatrix} =$

c. $3\begin{pmatrix} 1 & 2 \\ 3 & 4 \end{pmatrix} + 2\begin{pmatrix} 4 & -3 \\ -2 & 1 \end{pmatrix} =$

Exercise 4.2. $_m(a_{ij})_n + c_m(b_{ij})_n =$

Exercise 4.3. Find a basis for the vector space of all 2×3 matrices over $\mathscr{R}$.

MULTIPLICATION OF MATRICES

At the beginning of this chapter we applied a linear transformation of $\mathscr{V}_3(\mathscr{S})$ to $\mathscr{V}_3(\mathscr{S})$, represented by equations (1). If we now apply a second transformation of $\mathscr{V}_3(\mathscr{S})$ to $\mathscr{V}_3(\mathscr{S})$, transforming the η_i's into a basis ζ_i, $(i = 1,2,3)$, we can express the η_i's as linear combinations of the ζ_i's explicitly by

$$
\begin{aligned}
\eta_1 &= b_{11}\zeta_1 + b_{12}\zeta_2 + b_{13}\zeta_3 \\
\eta_2 &= b_{21}\zeta_1 + b_{22}\zeta_2 + b_{23}\zeta_3 \\
\eta_3 &= b_{31}\zeta_1 + b_{32}\zeta_2 + b_{33}\zeta_3
\end{aligned}
\tag{2}
$$

By Definition 3.3 the transformation directly from the ξ_i's to the ζ_i's is a linear transformation represented by

$$
\begin{aligned}
\xi_1 &= c_{11}\zeta_1 + c_{12}\zeta_2 + c_{13}\zeta_3 \\
\xi_2 &= c_{21}\zeta_1 + c_{22}\zeta_2 + c_{23}\zeta_3 \\
\xi_3 &= c_{31}\zeta_1 + c_{32}\zeta_2 + c_{33}\zeta_3
\end{aligned}
\tag{3}
$$

To determine the c_{ij}'s in terms of the a_{ij}'s and the b_{ij}'s, we substitute the η_i's from equations (2) into equations (1) and obtain

$$\xi_i = a_{i1}(b_{11}\zeta_1 + b_{12}\zeta_2 + b_{13}\zeta_3) + a_{i2}(b_{21}\zeta_1 + b_{22}\zeta_2 + b_{23}\zeta_3)$$
$$+ a_{i3}(b_{31}\zeta_1 + b_{32}\zeta_2 + b_{33}\zeta_3)$$

$$= (a_{i1}b_{11} + a_{i2}b_{21} + a_{i3}b_{31})\zeta_1 + (a_{i1}b_{12} + a_{i2}b_{22} + a_{i3}b_{32})\zeta_2$$
$$+ (a_{i1}b_{13} + a_{i2}b_{23} + a_{i3}b_{33})\zeta_3, \text{ for } i = 1, 2, 3$$

(4)

Comparing equations (4) and (3), we see that $c_{ij} = a_{i1}b_{1j} + a_{i2}b_{2j} + a_{i3}b_{3j}$. Corresponding to the transformation determined by equations (1), (2), and (3), we have the matrices A, B, and C, respectively. Since according to Definition 3.3 the transformation determined by equations (3) is the product of the transformation determined by equations (1) and (2), it is natural to call the matrix C the product AB of matrices A and B. We note further (using Definition 4.2) that $c_{ij} = \alpha_{ri} \cdot \beta_{cj}$. In generalizing this result, we recall that the scalar product is defined only for two vectors of the same order. Thus α_{ri} and β_{cj} must be vectors of the same order. But this means that the number of columns in matrix A must be equal to the number of rows in matrix B in order for the product to exist.

▶DEFINITION 4.6. *Matrix multiplication.* The *product* $_m(a_{ij})_n$ times $_n(b_{ij})_p$ is the matrix $_m(c_{ij})_p$, $[_m(a_{ij})_n \cdot {}_n(b_{ij})_p = {}_m(c_{ij})_p]$, where $c_{ij} = \alpha_{ri} \cdot \beta_{cj} = \sum_{k=1}^{n} a_{ik}b_{kj}$, $(i = 1, 2, \ldots, m; j = 1, 2, \ldots, p)$.

For example,

$$\begin{pmatrix} 1 & 2 \\ 3 & 4 \end{pmatrix}\begin{pmatrix} 0 & -1 \\ 2 & 1 \end{pmatrix} = \begin{pmatrix} 1 \cdot 0 + 2 \cdot 2 & 1(-1) + 2 \cdot 1 \\ 3 \cdot 0 + 4 \cdot 2 & 3(-1) + 4 \cdot 1 \end{pmatrix}$$

$$= \begin{pmatrix} 4 & 1 \\ 8 & 1 \end{pmatrix}$$

However,

$$\begin{pmatrix} 0 & -1 \\ 2 & 1 \end{pmatrix}\begin{pmatrix} 1 & 2 \\ 3 & 4 \end{pmatrix} = \begin{pmatrix} -3 & -4 \\ 5 & 8 \end{pmatrix}$$

This example is sufficient to show that AB is not necessarily equal to BA and to prove the following theorem, even in the case where both AB and BA exist.

▶**THEOREM 4.3.** Matrix multiplication is not commutative.

▶**THEOREM 4.4.** Matrix multiplication is associative.

PROOF: Exercise.

▶**THEOREM 4.5.** Matrix multiplication is $\begin{Bmatrix} \text{left} \\ \text{right} \end{Bmatrix}$ distributive with respect to matrix addition.

PROOF: To prove left distributivity, let A be an $m \times n$ matrix over $\mathscr{S}$ and B and C be $n \times p$ matrices over $\mathscr{S}$. Then

$$A(B + C) = (a_{ij})[(b_{ij}) + (c_{ij})] = (a_{ij})(b_{ij} + c_{ij})$$
$$= \left(\sum_{k=1}^{n} a_{ik}[b_{kj} + c_{kj}] \right)$$
$$= \left(\sum_{k=1}^{n} a_{ik}b_{kj} + \sum_{k=1}^{n} a_{ik}c_{kj} \right)$$
$$= \left(\sum_{k=1}^{n} a_{ik}b_{kj} \right) + \left(\sum_{k=1}^{n} a_{ik}c_{kj} \right)$$
$$= (a_{ij})(b_{ij}) + (a_{ij})(c_{ij}) = AB + AC$$

The proof of right distributivity is similar.

▶**DEFINITION 4.7.** The $n \times n$ matrix over $\mathscr{S}$ such that $a_{ij} = e_1$ for $i = j$ and $a_{ij} = e_0$ for $i \neq j$ is the $n \times n$ *identity matrix* over $\mathscr{S}$ denoted by I_n.

For example, over $\mathscr{R}$

$$I_n = \begin{pmatrix} 1 & 0 & 0 & . & . & . & 0 \\ 0 & 1 & 0 & . & . & . & 0 \\ 0 & 0 & 1 & . & . & . & 0 \\ . & & & & & & . \\ . & & & & & & . \\ . & & & & & & . \\ 0 & 0 & 0 & . & . & . & 1 \end{pmatrix}$$

▶ **THEOREM 4.6.** $_mA_nI_n = {}_mA_n$; $I_n\,{}_nB_p = {}_nB_p$.

PROOF: Exercise.

▶ **THEOREM 4.7.** I_n is the unique multiplicative identity in the set of all $n \times n$ matrices.

PROOF: By Theorem 4.6 $_nA_n \cdot I_n = I_n \cdot {}_nA_n = {}_nA_n$. To show the uniqueness, assume that J_n is a second multiplicative identity in the set of all $n \times n$ matrices. By definition of multiplicative identity, $I_n = I_n \cdot J_n = J_n$.

Exercise 4.4. Form the indicated products for the following matrices over $\mathscr{R}$.

a. $\begin{pmatrix} 1 & 2 & 3 \\ 4 & 5 & 6 \\ 7 & 8 & 9 \end{pmatrix}\begin{pmatrix} 1 & 2 & -1 \\ -2 & -4 & 2 \\ 1 & 2 & -1 \end{pmatrix}$

b. $\begin{pmatrix} 1 & 2 & -1 & 0 \\ 0 & 1 & 1 & -1 \end{pmatrix}\begin{pmatrix} 1 & 2 & 3 \\ -1 & 0 & 1 \\ 1 & 2 & -1 \\ 2 & -2 & 1 \end{pmatrix}$

Exercise 4.5. Show that the following is equivalent to Definition 4.7: The matrix over $\mathscr{S}$ with $\alpha_{ri} = \epsilon_i (i = 1, 2, \ldots, n)$ in $\mathscr{V}_n(\mathscr{S})$ is the $n \times n$ identity matrix over $\mathscr{S}$.

Exercise 4.6. Let $A = \begin{pmatrix} 1 & 0 & -2 \\ 2 & 3 & -1 \end{pmatrix}$ and $B = \begin{pmatrix} 2 & -1 \\ 1 & 1 \\ 0 & -2 \end{pmatrix}$. Find AB and BA.

Exercise 4.7. Form the indicated products for the following matrices over $\mathscr{J}_5$.

a. $\begin{pmatrix} 1 & 2 & 3 \\ 4 & 0 & 1 \\ 2 & 3 & 4 \end{pmatrix}\begin{pmatrix} 1 & 2 & 4 \\ 3 & 1 & 2 \\ 1 & 2 & 4 \end{pmatrix}$

b. $\begin{pmatrix} 1 & 4 & 1 & 2 \\ 2 & 0 & 2 & 3 \\ 3 & 1 & 4 & 1 \end{pmatrix}\begin{pmatrix} 1 & 0 \\ 2 & 1 \\ 4 & 1 \\ 0 & 4 \end{pmatrix}$

Exercise 4.8. Denoting $AAA \cdots A$ (k factors) by A^k, prove that $A^3 = Z$ when

$$A = \begin{pmatrix} e_0 & e_0 & e_0 \\ a & e_0 & e_0 \\ b & c & e_0 \end{pmatrix}$$

Exercise 4.9. If p and q are positive integers, prove $_nA_n^p \cdot {}_nA_n^q = {}_nA_n^{p+q}$.

Exercise 4.10. If p and q are positive integers, prove $[_nA_n^p]^q = {}_nA_n^{pq}$.

Exercise 4.11. Define $_nA_n^0$ so that the laws in the two previous exercises hold if p and q are nonnegative integers.

RANK OF A MATRIX

▶**DEFINITION 4.8.** The $\begin{Bmatrix} \text{row} \\ \text{column} \end{Bmatrix}$ rank of a matrix A is equal to the maximal number of linearly independent $\begin{Bmatrix} \text{row} \\ \text{column} \end{Bmatrix}$ vectors in A.

▶**LEMMA 4.1.** Interchanging two $\begin{Bmatrix} \text{rows} \\ \text{columns} \end{Bmatrix}$ of a matrix does not change the row or column rank.

PROOF: That interchanging two rows does not change the row rank is obvious. Interchanging the ith and jth rows of a matrix simply interchanges the ith and jth components of each column vector. But this clearly affects neither the linear independence nor the linear dependence of these vectors and hence does not change the column rank. Similarly, interchanging two columns of a matrix changes neither row nor column rank.

▶**LEMMA 4.2.** Adding a multiple of a $\begin{Bmatrix} \text{row} \\ \text{column} \end{Bmatrix}$ to another $\begin{Bmatrix} \text{row} \\ \text{column} \end{Bmatrix}$ of a matrix does not change the $\begin{Bmatrix} \text{column} \\ \text{row} \end{Bmatrix}$ rank.

PROOF: Let $_mA_n = (a_{ij})$ and let B be the matrix obtained from A by adding a multiple of one row to another. Without loss of generality we shall add a times the 2nd row to the 1st row. If the column rank of A is n, it cannot increase. If the column rank, c, of A is less than n, then with $h = c + 1$, $\sum_{i=1}^{h} c_i\alpha_{ci} = \epsilon_0$ with not all $c_i = e_0$ $(i = 1,2, \ldots ,h)$. Then $\sum_{i=1}^{h} c_i a_{ki} = e_0$ for all $k = 1, 2, \ldots , m$. Hence

$$\sum_{i=1}^{h} c_i\beta_{ci} = \left(\sum_{i=1}^{h} c_i(a_{1i} + a\, a_{2i}), \sum_{i=1}^{h} c_i a_{2i}, \ldots, \sum_{i=1}^{h} c_i a_{mi} \right)$$

$$= \left(\sum_{i=1}^{h} c_i a_{1i} + a \sum_{i=1}^{h} c_i a_{2i}, \sum_{i=1}^{h} c_i a_{2i}, \ldots, \sum_{i=1}^{h} c_i a_{mi} \right) = \epsilon_0$$

Thus the first $c + 1$ columns of B are linearly dependent. But by Lemma 4.1 we can consider any $c + 1$ columns as the first $c + 1$ columns. Hence any $c + 1$ columns of B are linearly dependent and the column rank of B is less than or equal to c. Thus the column rank of B is less than or equal to the column rank of A.

Adding $-a$ times the second row of B to the first row of B, we obtain A. Thus by the above argument we have the column rank of A less than or equal to the column rank of B. Hence the column ranks of A and B are equal.

Similarly, it can be shown that adding a multiple of a column to another column of a matrix does not change the row rank.

▶ **LEMMA 4.3.** Adding a multiple of one $\left\{ \begin{matrix} \text{row} \\ \text{column} \end{matrix} \right\}$ to another $\left\{ \begin{matrix} \text{row} \\ \text{column} \end{matrix} \right\}$ of a matrix does not change the $\left\{ \begin{matrix} \text{row} \\ \text{column} \end{matrix} \right\}$ rank.

PROOF: Let B be the matrix obtained from matrix A by adding $b\alpha_{ri}$ to α_{rj}. By the corollary to Theorem 2.13 the row rank of B is not greater than the row rank of A. Adding $-b\beta_{ri}$ to β_{ri}, we obtain A from B. Hence the row rank of A is not greater than the row rank of B and the row ranks are equal. The proof for columns is similar.

▶**LEMMA 4.4.** If one $\left\{ \begin{array}{c} \text{row} \\ \text{column} \end{array} \right\}$ is a linear combination of the other $\left\{ \begin{array}{c} \text{rows} \\ \text{columns} \end{array} \right\}$ of a matrix, then replacing each element of that $\left\{ \begin{array}{c} \text{row} \\ \text{column} \end{array} \right\}$ by e_0 changes neither column nor row rank.

PROOF: Exercise.

▶**THEOREM 4.8.** The row rank of a matrix A is equal to the column rank of A.

PROOF: Let A be an $m \times n$ matrix whose row rank is r and whose column rank is c. This means that A has r linearly independent rows and c linearly independent columns. Rearrange the rows so that the first r rows are linearly independent, and then rearrange the columns so that the first c columns are linearly independent. By Lemma 4.1 neither row nor column rank is changed. The last $m - r$ rows of the new matrix are linear combinations of the first r rows; hence by $m - r$ applications of Lemma 4.4 we can obtain a new matrix having all elements in the last $m - r$ rows equal to e_0 and both ranks still unchanged. Since only the first r elements of the c linearly independent columns can be different from e_0, not more than r of these columns can be linearly independent. Thus we have $c \leq r$. Similarly, all elements of the last $n - c$ columns can be made e_0, and thus we have $r \leq c$. Hence $r = c$.

▶**DEFINITION 4.9.** The common row rank and column rank of a matrix A is called the *rank* of A and is denoted by $r(A)$.

By virtue of this definition, the following two theorems are direct consequences of Lemmas 4.1 and 4.2 and Theorem 4.6.

▶**THEOREM 4.9.** Interchanging two $\left\{\begin{matrix} \text{rows} \\ \text{columns} \end{matrix}\right\}$ of a matrix does not change the rank.

▶**THEOREM 4.10.** Adding a multiple of one $\left\{\begin{matrix} \text{row} \\ \text{column} \end{matrix}\right\}$ to another $\left\{\begin{matrix} \text{row} \\ \text{column} \end{matrix}\right\}$ of a matrix does not change the rank.

Exercise 4.12. Show that $r(I_n) = n$.

Exercise 4.13. Does there exist an $m \times n$ matrix of rank 0?

Exercise 4.14. Find the ranks of the following matrices over $\mathscr{R}$.

a.
$$A = \begin{pmatrix} 1 & 2 & 3 \\ 1 & 0 & 1 \\ 2 & 4 & 6 \end{pmatrix}$$

b.
$$B = \begin{pmatrix} 1 & 2 & 3 \\ 4 & 5 & 6 \\ 7 & 8 & 9 \end{pmatrix}$$

c. $A + B$.

d. AB and BA.

Exercise 4.15. Show that $r(_mA_n) \le \min(m,n)$.

Exercise 4.16. If $C = AB$, show that $r(C) \le \min[r(A),r(B)]$. (*Hint:* Use the corollary to Theorem 2.13.)

Exercise 4.17. Defining the *transpose* of a matrix $A = {}_m(a_{ij})_n$ to be the matrix $A^T = {}_n(b_{ij})_m$, where $b_{ij} = a_{ji}$ for all i and j, show that $r(A) = r(A^T)$.

NONSINGULAR MATRICES

▶**DEFINITION 4.10.** An $m \times n$ matrix A is *nonsingular* if and only if $r(A) = \max(m,n)$. Otherwise the matrix is *singular*.

For example, I_n is a nonsingular matrix, while $\begin{pmatrix} a & a \\ a & a \end{pmatrix}$ is singular since its rank is 1. Furthermore, it follows from the definition that any $m \times n$ matrix with $m \ne n$ is singular.

►THEOREM 4.11. If C = AB and either A or B is nonsingular, then $r(C) = \min [r(A), r(B)]$.

PROOF: Suppose $_nB_n$ is nonsingular so that $r(B) = n$. Then A must be an $m \times n$ matrix. Letting $r(A) = u$, we have $u \leq n$ since A has only n columns. Let A be rewritten if necessary so that its first u rows are linearly independent. Let α_{ri} denote the ith row vector of A, β_{ri} denote the ith row vector of B and γ_{ri} the ith row vector of C. Then computation shows $\gamma_{ri} = \sum_{k=1}^{n} a_{ik}\beta_{rk}$ $(i = 1, 2, \ldots, n)$, i.e., the rows of C are linear combinations of the rows of B. Since the rows of B are linearly independent, $\gamma_{ri} = \epsilon_0$ only if $a_{ik} = 0$ for all $k = 1, 2, \ldots, n$, i.e., $\alpha_{ri} = \epsilon_0$. But A has at least u nonzero rows; hence C also does.

Consider a linear combination of the first u rows of C: $\sum_{i=1}^{u} s_i\gamma_{ri} = \epsilon_0$. We have

$$\sum_{i=1}^{u} s_i\gamma_{ri} = \sum_{i=1}^{u} s_i \sum_{k=1}^{n} a_{ik}\beta_{rk} = \sum_{i=1}^{u} \sum_{k=1}^{n} s_i a_{ik}\beta_{rk} = \epsilon_0$$

Since the β_{rk} are linearly independent, we have $\sum_{i=1}^{u} s_i a_{ik} = e_0$ for $k = 1, 2, \ldots, n$, from which it follows that $\sum_{i=1}^{u} s_i\alpha_{ri} = \epsilon_0$. But since the first u of the α_{ri} are linearly independent, we have $s_i = e_0$ $(i = 1, 2, \ldots, u)$. Thus the first u of the γ_{ri}'s are linearly independent. Thus $r(C) \geq u$. But by Exercise 4.16 we have $r(C) \leq u$. Hence $r(C) = u = \min [r(A), r(B)]$. If A is the nonsingular matrix, a similar argument using the columns of C shows that $r(C) = \min [r(A), r(B)]$.

►COROLLARY. If AB = Z and A is nonsingular, then B = Z.

►THEOREM 4.12. If AB = Z, then either A or B is singular.

PROOF: Exercise.

▶**THEOREM 4.13.** The product of two $n \times n$ nonsingular matrices is a nonsingular matrix.

PROOF: Exercise.

▶**COROLLARY.** If A is nonsingular, then A^k is nonsingular.

Exercise 4.18. Discuss the singularity of the matrices in Exercise 4.14.

Exercise 4.19. Is the product of two singular matrices always singular?

Exercise 4.20. Is the product of two singular $n \times n$ matrices always singular?

INVERSE OF A MATRIX

▶**DEFINITION 4.11.** If for $_nA_n$ there exists $_nB_n$ such that $AB = BA = I$, then B is called the *inverse of* A and is denoted by A^{-1}.

▶**THEOREM 4.14.** If A^{-1} exists, it is unique.

PROOF: Let $_nB_n$ be a second inverse of A. Then using the associativity of matrix multiplication, we have $A^{-1} = A^{-1}I = A^{-1}(AB) = (A^{-1}A)B = IB = B$.

▶**THEOREM 4.15.** A square matrix has an inverse if and only if it is nonsingular.

PROOF: Part 1. Let A be an $n \times n$ singular matrix; then $r(A) < n$, hence $r(AB) < n$. But $r(I_n) = n$; thus $r(AB) \neq r(I_n)$ and $AB \neq I_n$. Therefore no singular matrix has an inverse, and we have proved the "only if" part of the theorem.

Part 2. Now suppose A is a nonsingular $n \times n$ matrix. Consider the set of $n \times n$ matrices A, A^2, A^3, ..., A^{n^2+1}. Since $n^2 + 1$ vectors in a space of dimension n^2 must be linearly dependent, we have

$$\sum_{i=1}^{n^2+1} a_i A^i = Z$$

with at least two $a_i \neq e_0$. Let k be the least value of i for which $a_i \neq e_0$. Then

$$\sum_{i=k}^{n^2+1} a_i A^i = Z$$

Whence

$$A^k \sum_{i=k}^{n^2+1} a_i A^{i-k} = Z$$

Since A^k is nonsingular by the corollary to Theorem 4.13, then by the corollary to Theorem 4.11,

$$\sum_{i=k}^{n^2+1} a_i A^{i-k} = Z \quad \text{or} \quad a_k I_n + \sum_{i=k+1}^{n^2+1} a_i A^{i-k} = Z$$

Since $a_k \neq e_0$,

$$I_n = -a_k^{-1} \sum_{i=k+1}^{n^2+1} a_i A^{i-k} = A\left[-a_k^{-1} \sum_{i=k+1}^{n^2+1} a_i A^{i-k-1} \right]$$

$$= \left[-a_k^{-1} \sum_{i=k+1}^{n^2+1} a_i A^{i-k-1} \right] A$$

Thus

$$-a_k^{-1} \sum_{i=k+1}^{n^2+1} a_i A^{i-k-1}$$

is by definition the inverse of A.

For a nonsingular matrix A we can extend the definition of A^k to negative integral exponents by means of the inverse of A. That is, $A^{-k} = (A^{-1})^k$.

Exercise 4.21. Show that $(AB)^{-1} = B^{-1}A^{-1}$, where defined.

Exercise 4.22. Show that the laws of exponents as stated in Exercises 4.9 and 4.10 now hold for all integral exponents.

Exercise 4.23. Show that I_n is its own inverse.

Exercise 4.24. Show that the inverse of the $n \times n$ matrix whose columns are the $\epsilon_i (i = 1,2, \ldots ,n)$ in an arbitrary order is the matrix whose rows are the ϵ_i in the same order.

Exercise 4.25. Show that over $\mathcal{R}$

$$\begin{pmatrix} 1 & 0 & 2 & 0 \\ 2 & 1 & 0 & 0 \\ 0 & 0 & 1 & -1 \\ 3 & 0 & 0 & 7 \end{pmatrix} \text{ is the inverse of } \begin{pmatrix} 7 & 0 & -14 & -2 \\ -14 & 1 & 28 & 4 \\ -3 & 0 & 7 & 1 \\ -3 & 0 & 6 & 1 \end{pmatrix}$$

Exercise 4.26. Show that the inverse of A^{-1} is A.

Exercise 4.27. Using the method of the proof of Theorem 4.15, find the inverse of $\begin{pmatrix} 1 & 2 \\ 1 & 1 \end{pmatrix}$ over $\mathcal{R}$. Over $\mathcal{J}_3$.

CHAPTER V

Systems of Linear Equations

INTRODUCTION

Consider the system of m linear equations in n unknowns:

$$
\begin{aligned}
a_{11}x_1 + a_{12}x_2 + \ldots + a_{1n}x_n &= b_1 \\
a_{21}x_1 + a_{22}x_2 + \ldots + a_{2n}x_n &= b_2 \\
&\ \ \vdots \\
a_{m1}x_1 + a_{m2}x_2 + \ldots + a_{mn}x_n &= b_m
\end{aligned}
\tag{1}
$$

In matrix notation this system becomes $AX = B$, where

$$
A = (a_{ij}) =
\begin{pmatrix}
a_{11} & a_{12} & \cdots & a_{1n} \\
a_{21} & a_{22} & \cdots & a_{2n} \\
\vdots & & & \vdots \\
a_{m1} & a_{m2} & \cdots & a_{mn}
\end{pmatrix}
\tag{2}
$$

is an $m \times n$ matrix of scalars and is called the *coefficient matrix* of the system (1). Also,

$$
X =
\begin{pmatrix}
x_1 \\
x_2 \\
\vdots \\
x_n
\end{pmatrix}
$$

which is an $n \times 1$ matrix.

$$B = \begin{pmatrix} b_1 \\ b_2 \\ \cdot \\ \cdot \\ \cdot \\ b_m \end{pmatrix}$$

which is an $m \times 1$ matrix called the *constant matrix*.

If we consider the matrix equation as a linear equation in one unknown with real numbers as coefficients, it can be solved by multiplying both members by the inverse of A, provided A is not 0. Thus we have

$$AX = B$$
$$A^{-1}AX = A^{-1}B$$
$$X = A^{-1}B, \qquad (A \neq 0)$$

This suggests that we try the same approach in solving the matrix equation. However, the condition $A \neq 0$ for the linear equation becomes the condition that A is a nonsingular matrix when considering the solution of the matrix equation. This condition is necessary since by Theorem 4.15 matrix A has an inverse if and only if it is nonsingular.

Since $A^{-1}AX$ is not necessarily equal to AXA^{-1}, we must multiply by the inverse from the left. Multiplication from the $\begin{Bmatrix} \text{left} \\ \text{right} \end{Bmatrix}$ is called $\begin{Bmatrix} \text{premultiplication} \\ \text{postmultiplication} \end{Bmatrix}$.

NONSINGULAR COEFFICIENT MATRIX

▶**THEOREM 5.1.** A system of n linear equations in n unknowns with a nonsingular coefficient matrix has a unique solution.

PROOF: Write the system in matrix form to obtain $AX = B$. Then premultiply by A^{-1} (which exists by Theorem 4.15) to obtain $A^{-1}AX = A^{-1}B$ or $X = A^{-1}B$. This proves the existence. To prove the uniqueness, assume that there exists another solution Y. Hence $AY = B$, and, premultiplying by A^{-1}, we have $A^{-1}AY = A^{-1}B$ or $Y = A^{-1}B$. But since $A^{-1}B = X$, we have $Y = X$, and the solution is unique.

We now consider the system of n linear equations in n unknowns:

$$
\begin{aligned}
a_{11}x_1 + a_{12}x_2 + \ldots + a_{1n}x_n &= b_1 \\
a_{21}x_1 + a_{22}x_2 + \ldots + a_{2n}x_n &= b_2 \\
&\qquad\qquad\qquad\qquad\quad (3) \\
a_{n1}x_1 + a_{n2}x_2 + \ldots + a_{nn}x_n &= b_n
\end{aligned}
$$

Or the system may be written more compactly as

$$
\sum_{j=1}^{n} a_{ij}x_j = b_i \qquad (\text{for } i = 1,2,3,\ldots,n) \tag{4}
$$

In matrix notation the system becomes

$$
AX = B \tag{5}
$$

For the present discussion we shall assume that the coefficient matrix is nonsingular. Systems of equations having singular coefficient matrices will be discussed in a later section.

The following elementary transformations may be performed on a system of equations without altering the solutions:

(1) Multiplying an equation by a nonzero scalar.
(2) Adding a constant multiple of one equation to another equation.
(3) Interchanging two equations.

Since these transformations affect only the a_{ij} and the b_i, we can perform the same transformations within the matrices A and B. Specifically, transformations (1), (2), and (3) when applied to matrices become the *elementary matrix transformations:*

(1′) Multiplying a row by a nonzero scalar.
(2′) Adding a scalar times one row to another row.
(3′) Interchanging two rows.

The rank of a matrix is unaltered by the elementary matrix transformations. Since multiplying a vector by a nonzero scalar does not affect the linear independence of a set of vectors, the transformation (1′) cannot change the rank of a matrix. That the transformations (2′) and (3′) do not change the rank of a matrix was proven in Theorems 4.9 and 4.10.

In applying the transformations (1′), (2′), and (3′), we must be certain that the transformations are performed on A and B simultaneously. In order to facilitate this, let us define:

▶DEFINITION 5.1. The *augmented matrix* (A,B) of a system of equations is the matrix whose first n columns are identical with those of the coefficient matrix A and whose $(n + 1)$st column is the constant matrix B.

Thus the augmented matrix for the system (5) is

$$(A,B) = \begin{pmatrix} a_{11} & a_{12} & \cdots & a_{1n} & b_1 \\ a_{21} & a_{22} & \cdots & a_{2n} & b_2 \\ \cdot & & & & \cdot \\ \cdot & & & & \cdot \\ \cdot & & & & \cdot \\ a_{n1} & a_{n2} & \cdots & a_{nn} & b_n \end{pmatrix} \tag{6}$$

We now present a method of solution in which we use the transformations (1′), (2′), and (3′) to transform our system of equations into an equivalent system $CX = D$, in which the solution is obvious.

If we could obtain a *diagonal matrix* C of the form*

$$C = \begin{pmatrix} c_{11} & 0 & 0 & 0 & \ldots & 0 \\ 0 & c_{22} & 0 & 0 & \ldots & 0 \\ 0 & 0 & c_{33} & 0 & \ldots & 0 \\ \cdot & & & & & \cdot \\ \cdot & & & & & \cdot \\ \cdot & & & & & \cdot \\ 0 & 0 & 0 & 0 & \ldots & c_{nn} \end{pmatrix}$$

then the system of equations represented by $CX = D$ would be

$$\begin{aligned} c_{11}x_1 &&&= d_1 \\ & c_{22}x_2 && = d_2 \\ && \cdot & \\ && \cdot & \\ && \cdot & \\ && c_{nn}x_n = d_n \end{aligned} \tag{7}$$

Since we obtained the diagonal matrix C from the nonsingular matrix A by the use of the elementary matrix transformations which leave the rank unaltered, C is nonsingular. Thus $c_{ii} \neq 0$ $(i = 1, 2, \ldots, n)$, and the solution of the system is $x_i = d_i/c_{ii}$ $(i = 1, \ldots, n)$.

Our object will be to transform the A part of (A,B) into a diagonal matrix (i.e., we must obtain 0 elements both below and above the diagonal). We shall first obtain 0 elements below the diagonal.

If in (6) we add $-\dfrac{a_{21}}{a_{11}}$ times the first row to the second row, we obtain a 0 in the a_{21} position. Similarly, if we add $-\dfrac{a_{i1}}{a_{11}}$ times the first row to the ith row, we obtain a 0 in the a_{i1} position for $i = 3, 4, \ldots, n$. Thus we have 0's below the first element in the first column. Next, using the second row of the new matrix in a similar manner, we obtain 0's below the diagonal

---

* To simplify the notation in future discussions, we shall use 0 and 1 in place of e_0 and e_1, respectively, regardless of which system of scalars is involved. We shall also use a/b to denote ab^{-1}.

element in the second column without altering the first column. Continuing, we obtain a matrix in which all elements below the diagonal are 0, i.e.,

$$\begin{pmatrix} a_{11} & a_{12} & a_{13} & \cdots & a_{1i} & \cdots & a_{1n} & b_1 \\ 0 & a'_{22} & a'_{23} & \cdots & a'_{2i} & \cdots & a'_{2n} & b'_2 \\ 0 & 0 & a'_{33} & \cdots & a'_{3i} & \cdots & a'_{3n} & b'_3 \\ \cdot & & & & & & & \cdot \\ \cdot & & & & & & & \cdot \\ \cdot & & & & & & & \cdot \\ 0 & 0 & 0 & \cdots & a'_{ii} & \cdots & a'_{in} & b'_i \\ \cdot & & & & & & & \cdot \\ \cdot & & & & & & & \cdot \\ \cdot & & & & & & & \cdot \\ 0 & 0 & 0 & \cdots & 0 & \cdots & a'_{nn} & b'_n \end{pmatrix} \tag{8}$$

If in the above procedure the diagonal element we are to divide by is 0, we interchange the row containing this 0 diagonal element with any subsequent row having a nonzero element in the ith column. The existence of such a nonzero element is shown by the following argument. If the diagonal element and all of the elements below the diagonal element in the ith column are 0, then the ith column is a linear combination of the first $(i-1)$ columns—a contradiction since the coefficient matrix is nonsingular.

By a similar process, beginning with the nth row and working upward, we obtain 0's above the diagonal in the first n columns.

Thus we have

$$\begin{pmatrix} a'_{11} & 0 & 0 & 0 & \cdots & 0 & b_1'' \\ 0 & a'_{22} & 0 & 0 & \cdots & 0 & b_2'' \\ 0 & 0 & a'_{33} & 0 & \cdots & 0 & b_3'' \\ \cdot & & & & & & \cdot \\ \cdot & & & & & & \cdot \\ \cdot & & & & & & \cdot \\ 0 & 0 & 0 & 0 & 0 \cdot\cdot & a'_{nn} & b_n'' \end{pmatrix} = (A', B'') \tag{9}$$

from which the solution

$$x_i = \frac{b_i''}{a_{ii}'} \qquad (i = 1,2,\ldots,n) \tag{10}$$

follows immediately.

Observe that the result would be the same if we performed, within the matrix (9), all of the divisions indicated in (10). That is, multiply the ith row by $(1/a_{ii}')$ $(i = 1,2,\ldots,n)$ to obtain

$$\begin{pmatrix} 1 & 0 & 0 & 0 & 0 & 0 & \ldots & 0 & x_1 \\ 0 & 1 & 0 & 0 & 0 & 0 & \ldots & 0 & x_2 \\ 0 & 0 & 1 & 0 & 0 & 0 & \ldots & 0 & x_3 \\ 0 & 0 & 0 & 1 & 0 & 0 & \ldots & 0 & x_4 \\ \cdot & & & & & & & & \cdot \\ \cdot & & & & & & & & \cdot \\ \cdot & & & & & & & & \cdot \\ 0 & 0 & 0 & 0 & 0 & 0 & \ldots & 1 & x_n \end{pmatrix} \tag{11}$$

In matrix notation we have transformed the augmented matrix (A,B) into the matrix (I_n,X_B) in which X_B is the solution for equation (5), $AX = B$.

Of course, the method outlined above is only one of many methods which might be used in solving a system of equations such as (5). This particular method of solution is known as the *Gaussian Elimination* method.

As an example, suppose we use the Gaussian Elimination method to solve the following system of equations:

$$\begin{aligned} 3x + 2y - z &= 4 \\ x - y + z &= 1 \\ 2x + y - 3z &= 0 \end{aligned} \tag{12}$$

The corresponding matrix equation is

$$\begin{pmatrix} 3 & 2 & -1 \\ 1 & -1 & 1 \\ 2 & 1 & -3 \end{pmatrix} \begin{pmatrix} x \\ y \\ z \end{pmatrix} = \begin{pmatrix} 4 \\ 1 \\ 0 \end{pmatrix} \tag{13}$$

and

$$(A,B) = \begin{pmatrix} 3 & 2 & -1 & 4 \\ 1 & -1 & 1 & 1 \\ 2 & 1 & -3 & 0 \end{pmatrix}$$

is the augmented matrix.

Recall that the plan of solution demands that we transform the A part of (A,B) into a diagonal matrix. To accomplish this, we employ transformation (2') repeatedly, as outlined above. First, in order to produce 0 elements below the diagonal element in the first column of (A,B), we add $-\frac{1}{3}$ times the first row to the second row and add $-\frac{2}{3}$ times the first row to the third row to obtain the following matrix:

$$\begin{pmatrix} 3 & 2 & -1 & 4 \\ 0 & -\frac{5}{3} & \frac{4}{3} & -\frac{1}{3} \\ 0 & -\frac{1}{3} & -\frac{7}{3} & -\frac{8}{3} \end{pmatrix}$$

Now, to produce a 0 below the diagonal element in the second column of this matrix, add $-\frac{1}{5}$ times the second row to the third row to obtain the matrix

$$\begin{pmatrix} 3 & 2 & -1 & 4 \\ 0 & -\frac{5}{3} & \frac{4}{3} & -\frac{1}{3} \\ 0 & 0 & -\frac{39}{15} & -\frac{39}{15} \end{pmatrix}$$

We now have a matrix in which all of the elements below the diagonal elements are 0, and according to the plan of solution we proceed to produce 0's above the diagonal elements. Beginning with the third row, we produce 0's above the diagonal by adding $\frac{20}{39}$ times the third row to the second row and by adding $-\frac{15}{39}$ times the third row to the first row to obtain the matrix

$$\begin{pmatrix} 3 & 2 & 0 & 5 \\ 0 & -\frac{5}{3} & 0 & -\frac{5}{3} \\ 0 & 0 & -\frac{39}{15} & -\frac{39}{15} \end{pmatrix}$$

Now, by adding $\frac{6}{5}$ times the second row to the first row of this matrix, we obtain the desired matrix

$$\begin{pmatrix} 3 & 0 & 0 & 3 \\ 0 & -\frac{5}{3} & 0 & -\frac{5}{3} \\ 0 & 0 & -\frac{39}{15} & -\frac{39}{15} \end{pmatrix}$$

To obtain the final simplification, multiply the first row by $\frac{1}{3}$, the second row by $-\frac{3}{5}$, and the third row by $-\frac{15}{39}$ to obtain the matrix

$$\begin{pmatrix} 1 & 0 & 0 & 1 \\ 0 & 1 & 0 & 1 \\ 0 & 0 & 1 & 1 \end{pmatrix}$$

This is the augmented matrix corresponding to the matrix equation

$$\begin{pmatrix} 1 & 0 & 0 \\ 0 & 1 & 0 \\ 0 & 0 & 1 \end{pmatrix} \begin{pmatrix} x \\ y \\ z \end{pmatrix} = \begin{pmatrix} 1 \\ 1 \\ 1 \end{pmatrix} \quad \text{or} \quad I_3 \begin{pmatrix} x \\ y \\ z \end{pmatrix} = \begin{pmatrix} 1 \\ 1 \\ 1 \end{pmatrix} \quad (14)$$

from which $x = 1$, $y = 1$, and $z = 1$. Thus we have solved the system (12).

Note that rigid adherence to the plan of solution as outlined involves working with fractions to a considerable degree. This situation could be avoided by judicious use of transformations (1') and (3') along with (2'). For example, the interchange of row one and row two in (A,B) yields the matrix

$$\begin{pmatrix} 1 & -1 & 1 & 1 \\ 3 & 2 & -1 & 4 \\ 2 & 1 & -3 & 0 \end{pmatrix}$$

Beginning with this matrix and using (2') with integral multipliers, we obtain 0's below the diagonal element in row one.

The resulting matrix is

$$\begin{pmatrix} 1 & -1 & 1 & 1 \\ 0 & 5 & -4 & 1 \\ 0 & 3 & -5 & -2 \end{pmatrix}$$

Now before attempting to produce a 0 below the diagonal element in row two, we might simplify the operation by adding -2 times row three to row two to obtain

$$\begin{pmatrix} 1 & -1 & 1 & 1 \\ 0 & -1 & 6 & 5 \\ 0 & 3 & -5 & -2 \end{pmatrix}$$

Using this matrix, add 3 times row two to row three to obtain

$$\begin{pmatrix} 1 & -1 & 1 & 1 \\ 0 & -1 & 6 & 5 \\ 0 & 0 & 13 & 13 \end{pmatrix}$$

Here it is obvious that the process of producing 0 elements above the diagonal elements will be simplified if we first multiply row three by $\frac{1}{13}$. Looking ahead, we are also prompted to multiply row two by -1. We then have

$$\begin{pmatrix} 1 & -1 & 1 & 1 \\ 0 & 1 & -6 & -5 \\ 0 & 0 & 1 & 1 \end{pmatrix}$$

Now the work of obtaining 0's above the diagonal elements can be accomplished without encountering fractions, and we have, as before, the matrix

$$\begin{pmatrix} 1 & 0 & 0 & 1 \\ 0 & 1 & 0 & 1 \\ 0 & 0 & 1 & 1 \end{pmatrix}$$

Using the Gaussian Elimination method, solve the following systems of equations over $\mathscr{R}$.

Exercise 5.1.

$$\begin{aligned} x + y + z + w &= 4 \\ x - y + z + w &= 0 \\ x \phantom{{}+y} - z + w &= -2 \\ x \phantom{{}+y+z} - w &= -6 \end{aligned}$$

Ans. $x = -3$
$y = 2$
$z = 2$
$w = 3$

Exercise 5.2.

$$\begin{aligned} x + y + z + 2w &= -3 \\ x + 2y + z + 3w &= -2 \\ x - 2y + z - 5w &= 2 \\ 2x - y + 3z - 4w &= -2 \end{aligned}$$

Ans. $x = 1$
$y = 3$
$z = -3$
$w = -2$

Exercise 5.3.

$$\begin{aligned} x + y + z + w &= -8 \\ x - y + z + w &= 0 \\ x \phantom{{}+y} - z + w &= 4 \\ x \phantom{{}+y+z} - w &= 2 \end{aligned}$$

Ans. $x = 1$
$y = -4$
$z = -4$
$w = -1$

Exercise 5.4.

$$\begin{aligned} 3x + y - z - 3u + v &= 6 \\ x + 2y - 3z - 6u + 2v &= 9 \\ 4x + 3y + 2z - 9u + 2v &= 2 \\ x + y - z + 2u + v &= 4 \\ 2x + y + 3z - 3u + v &= -3 \end{aligned}$$

MATRIX INVERSION BY GAUSSIAN ELIMINATION

In Exercises 5.1 and 5.3 the coefficient matrices are identical and in the process of solution the same operations were performed in each case. Both solutions could have been obtained simultaneously if the *doubly augmented* matrix

$$(A, B_1, B_2) = \begin{pmatrix} 1 & 1 & 1 & 1 & 4 & -8 \\ 1 & -1 & 1 & 1 & 0 & 0 \\ 1 & 0 & -1 & 1 & -2 & 4 \\ 1 & 0 & 0 & -1 & -6 & 2 \end{pmatrix}$$

had been used instead of the two separate matrices

$$(A,B_1) = \begin{pmatrix} 1 & 1 & 1 & 1 & 4 \\ 1 & -1 & 1 & 1 & 0 \\ 1 & 0 & -1 & 1 & -2 \\ 1 & 0 & 0 & -1 & -6 \end{pmatrix}$$

and

$$(A,B_2) = \begin{pmatrix} 1 & 1 & 1 & 1 & -8 \\ 1 & -1 & 1 & 1 & 0 \\ 1 & 0 & -1 & 1 & 4 \\ 1 & 0 & 0 & -1 & 2 \end{pmatrix}$$

Thus, in general, if we have given the following k systems of n equations in n unknowns, all having the same coefficient matrix,

$$
\begin{aligned}
AX &= B_1 \\
AX &= B_2 \\
AX &= B_3 \\
&\cdot \qquad \cdot \\
&\cdot \qquad \cdot \\
&\cdot \qquad \cdot \\
AX &= B_k
\end{aligned}
\tag{15}
$$

we can obtain the solutions to all of the systems simultaneously by transforming the matrix $(A,B_1,B_2, \ldots ,B_k)$ into the matrix $(I_n,X_{B_1},X_{B_2}, \ldots ,X_{B_k})$.

We have defined the inverse of a nonsingular matrix and have proved its existence. We now can make use of Gaussian Elimination to obtain the inverse of such a matrix. Since the solution of $AX = I_n$ is $X = A^{-1}$, the inverse of A, we apply the above method to the $n \times 2n$ matrix (A,I_n) and obtain the matrix (I_n,A^{-1}). Thus we have determined A^{-1}, the inverse of the nonsingular square matrix A. Now that we have a method for finding the inverse of a matrix, it is possible to solve a system of equations by matrix multiplication as outlined at the beginning of this chapter.

Exercise 5.5.   Find the inverse, A^{-1}, of the coefficient matrix A in Exercise 5.1.

Exercise 5.6.   Obtain the solutions to Exercises 5.1 and 5.3 by matrix multiplication.

Exercise 5.7.   Using the results of Exercise 5.5, verify that $AA^{-1} = A^{-1}A = I_4$.

SINGULAR COEFFICIENT MATRIX

If we have a system of n equations in n unknowns in which the coefficient matrix is singular and we apply Gaussian Elimination, we encounter a 0 diagonal element which cannot be removed by interchanging its row with a subsequent row. For otherwise we could determine the inverse of the coefficient matrix which, by Theorem 4.15, implies that the coefficient matrix is nonsingular. Suppose that, in spite of this, we begin the regular Gaussian Elimination procedure on a system of equations with a singular coefficient matrix. We shall ultimately encounter an impasse in the form of a 0 diagonal element without nonzero elements below it, i.e., an element $a_{ii} = 0$ such that $a_{ji} = 0$ for all $i < j \leq n$. We then proceed across the ith row to the first nonzero element of the coefficient matrix, i.e., some $a_{ik} \neq 0$ with $i < k \leq n$. If $a_{ik} = 0$ for $i < k \leq n$, then proceed immediately with steps outlined below covering this situation. Using this nonzero element a_{ik}, we produce 0's below it in its own column. (That is, we make $a_{jk} = 0$ for all $i < j \leq n$.) We then interchange the ith row and the kth row. The new ith row still has $a_{ji} = 0$ for all $i \leq j \leq n$. We repeat the above process using the first nonzero element to the right of a_{ii} in the ith row of the coefficient matrix.

Ultimately this procedure will produce an ith row all the elements of which in the coefficient matrix are 0. If the element

b_i is not 0, this row is equivalent to the equation $0x_1 + 0x_2 + \ldots + 0x_n = b_i \neq 0$, which clearly has no solution. In such a situation we say that the original system is *inconsistent* and has no solution. Nothing is to be gained by proceeding further.

In case $b_i = 0$ we go to the next diagonal element and proceed with Gaussian Elimination, using the above procedure each time we encounter a 0 diagonal element without nonzero elements below it. This eventually produces a matrix with all 0's below the diagonal and one or more rows made up entirely of 0's.

For example, suppose we wish to solve the system

$$
\begin{aligned}
v + 2w & & & & = 5 \\
2v + 4w & & & + z & = 11 \\
v + 2w + x + y & & & & = 4 \\
2v + 4w + x + y & & & & = 9 \\
v + 2w + x + y + z & & & & = 5
\end{aligned}
\tag{16}
$$

whose augmented matrix is

$$
\begin{pmatrix}
1 & 2 & 0 & 0 & 0 & 5 \\
2 & 4 & 0 & 0 & 1 & 11 \\
1 & 2 & 1 & 1 & 0 & 4 \\
2 & 4 & 1 & 1 & 0 & 9 \\
1 & 2 & 1 & 1 & 1 & 5
\end{pmatrix}
\tag{17}
$$

After producing 0's below the diagonal element in the first column, we have

$$
\begin{pmatrix}
1 & 2 & 0 & 0 & 0 & 5 \\
0 & 0 & 0 & 0 & 1 & 1 \\
0 & 0 & 1 & 1 & 0 & -1 \\
0 & 0 & 1 & 1 & 0 & -1 \\
0 & 0 & 1 & 1 & 1 & 0
\end{pmatrix}
\tag{18}
$$

We see that the diagonal element a_{22} is 0 and that there are no nonzero elements below it in the second column. We proceed across the second row to the first nonzero element (1 in the a_{25} position) and produce 0's below it.

$$\begin{pmatrix} 1 & 2 & 0 & 0 & 0 & 5 \\ 0 & 0 & 0 & 0 & 1 & 1 \\ 0 & 0 & 1 & 1 & 0 & -1 \\ 0 & 0 & 1 & 1 & 0 & -1 \\ 0 & 0 & 1 & 1 & 0 & -1 \end{pmatrix} \tag{19}$$

We then interchange the second and fifth rows to obtain

$$\begin{pmatrix} 1 & 2 & 0 & 0 & 0 & 5 \\ 0 & 0 & 1 & 1 & 0 & -1 \\ 0 & 0 & 1 & 1 & 0 & -1 \\ 0 & 0 & 1 & 1 & 0 & -1 \\ 0 & 0 & 0 & 0 & 1 & 1 \end{pmatrix} \tag{20}$$

Returning to the second row, we go across to the first nonzero element (1 in position a_{23}) and produce 0's below it to obtain

$$\begin{pmatrix} 1 & 2 & 0 & 0 & 0 & 5 \\ 0 & 0 & 1 & 1 & 0 & -1 \\ 0 & 0 & 0 & 0 & 0 & 0 \\ 0 & 0 & 0 & 0 & 0 & 0 \\ 0 & 0 & 0 & 0 & 1 & 1 \end{pmatrix} \tag{21}$$

We now interchange the second and third rows to obtain

$$\begin{pmatrix} 1 & 2 & 0 & 0 & 0 & 5 \\ 0 & 0 & 0 & 0 & 0 & 0 \\ 0 & 0 & 1 & 1 & 0 & -1 \\ 0 & 0 & 0 & 0 & 0 & 0 \\ 0 & 0 & 0 & 0 & 1 & 1 \end{pmatrix} \tag{22}$$

We now have all 0's in the second row of the coefficient matrix and $b_2 = 0$. Also we now happen to have all 0's below the diagonal.

To proceed with Gaussian Elimination, we would now like to produce all 0's above the diagonal. However, we can do this only where the diagonal element is not 0. We thus arrive at a coefficient matrix with two types of columns: (1) a nonzero diagonal element with all elements both below and above it 0; (2) a 0 diagonal element with no nonzero elements below it, but possibly with some nonzero elements above it.

It is now obvious that any column of type (2) is a linear combination of the columns of type (1). But the columns of type (1) are linearly independent; hence the rank r of the original coefficient matrix is the number of columns of type (1).

We now replace this matrix by the equivalent system of equations. Each variable corresponding to a column of type (2) is transposed to the right side. Then after dividing the ith equation by $a_{ii} \neq 0$, we have a solution expressing r unknowns in terms of the remaining $n - r$ unknowns.

Returning to our example, we see that matrix (22) happens to have only columns of type (1) and (2). Therefore we replace it by the equivalent system of equations

$$
\begin{aligned}
v + 2w \quad &= \quad 5 \\
0 &= \quad 0 \\
x + y \quad &= \quad -1 \\
0 &= \quad 0 \\
z \quad &= \quad 1
\end{aligned}
\tag{23}
$$

Since columns two and four of matrix (22) are of type (2), we transpose the w and y terms in (23) to the right side to obtain

$$
\begin{aligned}
v &= \quad 5 - 2w \\
x &= -1 - \ y \\
z &= 1
\end{aligned}
\tag{24}
$$

This gives us a solution involving three variables in terms of the remaining two. Since matrix (22) has three columns of type (1) and hence is of rank three, this is the type of solution to be expected.

The form of the solution as given in (24) is not unique since we might write

$$w = \frac{5 - v}{2}$$
$$y = -1 - x \qquad (25)$$
$$z = 1$$

In fact, a different method of solution might have given form (25) directly.

It is obvious that the solution of a system of equations is not altered if we add some new unknowns with 0 coefficients or if we add new equations of the form $0x_1 + 0x_2 + \ldots + 0x_n = 0$. Thus if we have a system of m equations in n unknowns with $m \neq n$, we shall simply add enough rows or columns of 0's to make the coefficient matrix square and then proceed as outlined above.

▶**THEOREM 5.2.** A *homogeneous system* of linear equations (i.e., one with a Z constant matrix) is consistent.

PROOF: Since the elements of the constant matrix are all 0, none of the elementary matrix transformations can introduce nonzero elements in the constant matrix. Therefore the system of equations cannot be inconsistent.

▶**THEOREM 5.3.** For a homogeneous system of linear equations whose $m \times n$ coefficient matrix has rank r, the system corresponding to the set of all solutions considered as nth order vectors is a vector space of dimension $n - r$.

PROOF: Without loss of generality, assume that the last $n - r$ unknowns were transposed to the right side in the process of solution. Thus a solution can be written as a vector $(x_1, x_2, \ldots, x_n)$, where

$$x_i = \sum_{j=r+1}^{n} b_{ij} x_j \ (i = 1, 2, \ldots, r)$$

$$x_i = x_i \ (i = r + 1, \ldots, n)$$

The verification that the system corresponding to this set of vectors is a vector space is left as an exercise. Let α_k $(k = 1, \ldots, n - r)$ be the solution with

$$x_{r+j} = \begin{cases} 1 \text{ for } j = k \\ 0 \text{ for } j \neq k \end{cases} \quad (j = 1, \ldots, n - r)$$

The α_i's are obviously linearly independent and hence the dimension of the vector space is at least $n - r$.

To show that any solution vector $(x_1, x_2, \ldots, x_n)$ is the linear combination $\sum_{j=1}^{n-r} x_{r+j} \alpha_j$ is left as an exercise. Thus the dimension is $n - r$.

In Exercises 5.8 through 5.14 find the solutions over $\mathscr{R}$ or show that the system is inconsistent.

Exercise 5.8.
$$\begin{aligned} x + y + z &= 3 \\ x - 2y + 3z &= -4 \\ x + 4y + 5z &= 10 \end{aligned}$$

Exercise 5.9.
$$\begin{aligned} x - y + z &= 1 \\ x + 2y - z &= 2 \\ 2x + y &= 1 \end{aligned}$$

Exercise 5.10.
$$\begin{aligned} w + 2x - y + z &= 6 \\ 2w - x + y + 2z &= 4 \\ w - 3x + 2y + z &= -2 \\ 5x - 3y &= 8 \end{aligned}$$

Exercise 5.11.
$$\begin{aligned} 3v + 2w + y &= 0 \\ w + x &= 0 \\ 5v + w + y &= 0 \\ 2v + x &= 0 \end{aligned}$$

Exercise 5.12.
$$v + 2w \qquad\qquad = 5$$
$$v + 2w + x + y = 4$$
$$2v + 4w + x + y = 9$$

Exercise 5.13.
$$x + y = 2$$
$$v - 2w + x + y = 0$$
$$-v - w + 2x + y = 3$$

Exercise 5.14.
$$x + y + z = 2$$
$$2x - y + 3z = -1$$
$$x + y - z = 0$$
$$x - 2y + z = -4$$
$$2x - y, \qquad = -4$$

Exercise 5.15. Solve the system in Exercise 5.11 over $\mathscr{J}_7$.

Exercise 5.16. Solve the system in Exercise 5.12 over $\mathscr{J}_{11}$.

Exercise 5.17. Find all vectors in $\mathscr{V}_3(\mathscr{R})$ orthogonal to $(1,1,1)$ and $(1,-2,3)$.

Exercise 5.18. Show that $(1,-1,2,3,2)$, $(0,1,1,-2,0)$, $(2,-1,4,0,1)$, $(1,2,1,-1,-3)$ and $(0,2,-1,1,1)$ are linearly independent over $\mathscr{R}$.

Exercise 5.19. Find a set of scalars to show that $(1,1,1,1)$, $(1,3,2,0)$, $(0,2,1,1)$, and $(4,3,1,0)$ are linearly dependent over $\mathscr{J}_5$.

Exercise 5.20. Let the *elementary matrices* U, V, and W be the result of applying the elementary matrix transformations $(1')$, $(2')$, and $(3')$, respectively, to the matrix I_m.

    a. Show that premultiplication of an $m \times n$ matrix A by U, V, and W results in the same matrix as applying $(1')$, $(2')$, and $(3')$, respectively, to A.

    b. Show that U, V, and W are nonsingular.

    c. Show that the rank of the products in part (a) is the same as the rank of A.

Exercise 5.21.

    a. For a system of equations with a nonsingular coefficient matrix A, show that Gaussian Elimination is equivalent to a sequence of premultiplications by elementary matrices.

    b. Show that the product of these elementary matrices is A^{-1}.

CHAPTER VI

Linear Programing

INTRODUCTION

In the calculus one discusses many problems in which the solution is a set of values for which a particular function of one or more variables attains a minimum or a maximum. In many applications such minimization or maximization problems are more complex. Besides the function for which an extremum is to be found, there are side conditions (constraints) to be satisfied. Some of the classical problems of this kind are discussed in the calculus of variations.

In this chapter we shall discuss one particular problem of this kind, namely, that in which the function to be minimized or maximized and the constraints are linear in the variables.

As an illustration, consider the following problem. A grain broker finds from long experience that in selling rice, corn, and wheat the following conditions prevail:

(1) He can sell five units of corn and rice together.
(2) He cannot sell more than six units of rice and wheat together.
(3) He always sells two more units of rice than he does of wheat.
(4) His profit per unit sold is $1 for corn, $2 for rice, and $3 for wheat.

How many units of each commodity should he sell in order to profit maximally?

In order to express these conditions mathematically, let the number of units of corn, rice, and wheat sold be denoted by

C, R, and W, respectively. Conditions (1), (2), (3), and (4) become

(1) $C + R \qquad = 5$
(2) $\qquad R + W \le 6$
(3) $\qquad R - W = 2$
(4) $C + 2R + 3W = \text{Profit}$

The problem is to find C, R, and W, all nonnegative, such that the profit is a maximum while the side conditions (1), (2), and (3) are satisfied. As we develop the algorithm for the solution of such linear programing problems, we shall use this example to facilitate the understanding of our discussion.

Returning to the general discussion, we find there is no loss of generality in considering only maximization problems, since a minimum for the function $f(x_1, x_2, \ldots, x_n)$ is a maximum for the function $-f(x_1, x_2, \ldots, x_n)$.

In most applications it is inherent that the variables may attain only nonnegative values. This again does not restrict generality, since a variable x which may attain nonpositive values only may be replaced by $-x$, and one which may attain negative as well as positive values may be replaced by $x_1 - x_2$ with x_1 and x_2 nonnegative.

THE LINEAR PROGRAMING PROBLEM

In mathematical terms the linear programing problem is to find a vector $\xi = (x_1, x_2, \ldots, x_n)$ in $\mathscr{V}_n(\mathscr{R}^\#)$ such that for matrices $_mB_n$ and $_mC_1$ over $\mathscr{R}^\#$, the constraints

(1) $x_j \ge 0 \qquad (j = 1, 2, \ldots, n)$
(2) $B\xi^T = C$

are satisfied and the linear function (called the *objective function*)

(3) $f(\xi) = \sum_{i=1}^{n} a_i x_i = \alpha \xi^T$

is maximized.* In the remainder of this chapter we shall always assume (1).

In practice it often happens that some constraints are inequalities. For example, we may have the constraint $b_{i1}x_1 + b_{i2}x_2 + \ldots + b_{ik}x_k \leq c_i$. To make an equation out of such an inequality we simply add another variable x_{k+1} to take up the "slack," that is, $b_{i1}x_1 + b_{i2}x_2 + \ldots + b_{ik}x_k + x_{k+1} = c_i$. Such a variable is called a *slack variable*. This slack variable appears in all other equations of (2) with a 0 coefficient. In order that the slack variable will not affect the objective function, we take $a_{k+1} = 0$ in (3). By adding a different slack variable for each inequality, we change all inequalities into equations.

A further assumption is that $c_i \geq 0$ $(i = 1,2,\ldots,m)$. This again is easily obtained by multiplying the constraint equations by -1, if necessary. Thus after the addition of slack variables as needed, and multiplying constraints by -1 where needed, we have the linear programing problem as stated above with the $c_i \geq 0$ $(i = 1,2,\ldots,m)$.

Let us consider the system of equations (2) without paying any attention to the maximization of $f(\xi)$. If this system of equations is inconsistent, there can, of course, be no solution to the linear programing problem. If the system of equations is consistent and has a unique solution, our problem is solved if all the x_i are nonnegative; otherwise the linear programing problem has no solution. In Chapter V we saw that if the system of equations (2) is consistent and does not have a unique solution it then has infinitely many solutions. Only in this case do we have the interesting problem of finding a solution with nonnegative x_i which maximizes $f(\xi)$. In order to assure this, there is no loss of generality in assuming $m < n$ for (2).

▶**DEFINITION 6.1.** A vector ξ over $\mathcal{V}_n(\mathcal{R}^\#)$ satisfying (1) and (2) is a *feasible solution*.

---

* Considering ξ as a $1 \times n$ matrix, ξ^T is the transpose of ξ as defined in Exercise 4.17.

▶**DEFINITION 6.2.** A feasible solution which maximizes the objective function is a *maximal solution*.

▶**DEFINITION 6.3.** A feasible solution with not more than m of the x_i positive is a *basic feasible solution*.

▶**DEFINITION 6.4.** A maximal solution which is a basic feasible solution is a *basic maximal solution*.

▶**THEOREM 6.1.** If ξ_1 and ξ_2 are feasible solutions, then the *convex combination* $a\xi_1 + (1 - a)\xi_2$ for $0 \leq a \leq 1$ is a feasible solution.

PROOF: Since $B\xi_1^T = C$ and $B\xi_2^T = C$, we have $B[a\xi_1 + (1 - a)\xi_2]^T = aB\xi_1^T + (1 - a)B\xi_2^T = aC + (1 - a)C = C$. Furthermore, since the components of ξ_1 and ξ_2 are non-negative, the components of $a\xi_1 + (1 - a)\xi_2$ are obviously nonnegative for all $0 \leq a \leq 1$.

▶**THEOREM 6.2.** If there exists more than one maximal solution, then there exist infinitely many maximal solutions.

PROOF: Let ξ_1 and ξ_2 be two maximal solutions such that $\alpha\xi_1^T = \alpha\xi_2^T = f_{\max}$. Then by Theorem 6.1 every *proper convex combination* $(0 < a < 1)$ of ξ_1 and ξ_2 is a feasible solution and is a different maximal solution since $\xi_1 \neq a\xi_1 + (1 - a)\xi_2 \neq \xi_2$ and $\alpha[q\xi_1 + (1 - a)\xi_2]^T = a\alpha\xi_1^T + (1 - a)\alpha\xi_2^T = af_{\max} + (1 - a)f_{\max} = f_{\max}$.

▶**DEFINITION 6.5.** An *extreme solution* is a feasible solution which cannot be written as a proper convex combination of two feasible solutions.

▶**THEOREM 6.3.** If for $k \leq m$, a set of k linearly independent column vectors of B can be found such that C is a linear combination of these with nonnegative scalars, then the vector ξ consisting of these scalars and 0's is an extreme solution.

PROOF: Without loss of generality, we assume the k linearly independent vectors to be the first k columns of $\mathbf{B}$. The hypothesis states that for $d_i \geq 0$ $(i = 1,2, \ldots ,k)$ $\sum_{i=1}^{k} d_i\beta_{ci} = \mathbf{C}^{\mathrm{T}}$. Thus $\xi = (d_1,d_2, \ldots ,d_k, 0,0, \ldots ,0)$ is a basic feasible solution. If ξ were not an extreme solution there would exist two different feasible solutions $\xi_1 = (x_1, \ldots ,x_n)$ and $\xi_2 = (y_1, \ldots ,y_n)$ with some $x_i \neq y_i$ such that for $0 < a < 1$, $\xi = a\xi_1 + (1 - a)\xi_2$, that is, $(d_1,d_2, \ldots ,d_k,0,0, \ldots ,0) = [ax_1 + (1 - a)y_1, \ldots ,ax_k + (1 - a)y_k, ax_{k+1} + (1 - a)y_{k+1}, \ldots ,ax_n + (1 - a)y_n]$. Since ξ_1 and ξ_2 are feasible, all x_i and y_i are nonnegative. Hence $x_j = y_j = 0$ $(j = k + 1, \ldots ,n)$, and ξ_1 and ξ_2 are basic feasible solutions. Thus $\sum_{i=1}^{k} x_i\beta_{ci} = \mathbf{C}^{\mathrm{T}}$ and $\sum_{i=1}^{k} y_i\beta_{ci} = \mathbf{C}^{\mathrm{T}}$. Subtracting the second expression from the first, we have $\sum_{i=1}^{k} (x_i - y_i)\beta_{ci} = \epsilon_0$, a contradiction to the hypothesis that the β_{ci} $(i = 1, \ldots ,k)$ are linearly independent. Thus ξ is an extreme solution.

▶ **THEOREM 6.4.** If ξ is an extreme solution, then the column vectors associated with the positive x_i are linearly independent. Thus, at most m of the x_i are positive.

PROOF: Without loss of generality, we let the first k of the x_i be positive, thus, $\sum_{i=1}^{k} x_i\beta_{ci} = \mathbf{C}^{\mathrm{T}}$. If the first k of the β_{ci} were linearly dependent, then there would exist d_i, not all 0, such that $\sum_{i=1}^{k} d_i\beta_{ci} = \epsilon_0$, and thus for any d we would have $\sum_{i=1}^{k} (x_i + dd_i) \beta_{ci} = \mathbf{C}^{\mathrm{T}}$ and $\sum_{i=1}^{k} (x_i - dd_i)\beta_{ci} = \mathbf{C}^{\mathrm{T}}$. For a positive d chosen small enough, none of the $(x_i + dd_i)$ and $(x_i - dd_i)$ are negative. Then $\xi_1 = (x_1 + dd_1, \ldots ,x_k + dd_k, 0, \ldots ,0)$ and $\xi_2 = (x_1 - dd_1, \ldots ,x_k - dd_k,0, \ldots ,0)$ are two feasible solutions and $\xi = \frac{1}{2}(\xi_1 + \xi_2)$. Since ξ is an extreme solution, this is a contradiction. Hence the k vectors β_{ci} are linearly independent.

▶**THEOREM 6.5.** There exist a finite number of extreme solutions.

PROOF: Exercise.

▶**THEOREM 6.6.** At least one extreme solution is a maximal solution.

PROOF: It is easily seen that any feasible solution can be written as a convex combination of the extreme solutions. Let the extreme solutions be $\xi_i (i = 1, \ldots, p)$. Let the maximal solution be $\xi_0 = \sum_{i=1}^{p} d_i \xi_i$ with $\sum_{i=1}^{p} d_i = 1$ and all $d_i \geq 0$. Then $\alpha \xi_0^{\mathrm{T}} = \alpha (\sum_{i=1}^{p} d_i \xi_i^{\mathrm{T}}) = \sum_{i=1}^{p} d_i \alpha \xi_i^{\mathrm{T}} = f_{\max}$.

Assuming ξ_0 not to be an extreme solution, we have $\alpha \xi_0^{\mathrm{T}} \geq \alpha \xi_i^{\mathrm{T}}$ $(i = 1, \ldots, p)$. Let ξ_m be a ξ_i such that $\alpha \xi_m^{\mathrm{T}} \geq \alpha \xi_i^{\mathrm{T}}$ $(i = 1, \ldots, p)$. Then it follows that $\alpha \xi_0^{\mathrm{T}} \leq \alpha \sum_{i=1}^{p} d_i \xi_m^{\mathrm{T}} = \alpha \xi_m^{\mathrm{T}}$, and, since ξ_0 is a maximal solution, $\alpha \xi_0^{\mathrm{T}} = \alpha \xi_m^{\mathrm{T}}$, i.e., the extreme solution ξ_m is a maximal solution.

From these theorems we see that if there exists a maximal solution there exists a basic maximal solution.

THE SIMPLEX METHOD

The solution to the linear programing problem is among its extreme solutions. Since by Theorem 6.5 there exist only a finite number of extreme solutions, the obvious approach of finding all extreme solutions to the system of equations (2) and then checking all these in (3) would give us a way of obtaining a solution to the linear programing problem. However, if m is large and n is much greater than m, this approach would be a tremendous undertaking. What one needs is a method by which one can proceed from a particular extreme solution to another extreme solution for which the objective function attains a larger value until a maximal solution is obtained. The so-called "simplex procedure" is such a method.

In order to start this procedure, one must first find an extreme solution. This in itself can be laborious since it is necessary to find m linearly independent columns of B such that C would be a linear combination of these columns with only non-negative scalars. However, if among the columns of B one could find all m columns of I_m, one could choose these columns. The c_i would be the necessary nonnegative scalars for the expression of C as a linear combination of these columns of B.

To make this always possible, we arbitrarily add some more variables to our system of equations in the following way: if the vector ϵ_i^T of $\mathscr{V}_m(\mathscr{R}^\#)$ is not among the columns of B, we add a variable y to every equation of (2). In the ith equation add y with a coefficient of 1 and in all other equations of (2) add y with a coefficient of 0. Such a variable is called an *artificial variable*. Obviously such an artificial variable should not appear with a nonzero value in the final maximal solution. To assure this, we add artificial variables to the objective function with coefficients of $-w$ where w is an arbitrarily large positive number. Thus our objective function cannot possibly attain its maximum as long as the extreme solution contains an artificial variable with a value greater than 0.

For uniformity in notation, let us restate our illustrative problem using x_1 for C, x_2 for R, and x_3 for W:

Maximize

$$x_1 + 2x_2 + 3x_3$$

subject to

$$x_1 + x_2 \qquad = 5$$
$$x_2 + x_3 \leq 6$$
$$x_2 - x_3 = 2$$

We begin by removing the inequality through introduction of x_4, a slack variable. The objective function is not altered and the constraints become

$$x_1 + x_2 \qquad \qquad = 5$$
$$x_2 + x_3 + x_4 = 6$$
$$x_2 - x_3 \qquad = 2$$

The matrix

$$B = \begin{pmatrix} 1 & 1 & 0 & 0 \\ 0 & 1 & 1 & 1 \\ 0 & 1 & -1 & 0 \end{pmatrix}$$

now needs ϵ_3^T of $\mathcal{V}_3(\mathcal{R}^\#)$ to have every column of I_3 among its columns. Thus we add the artificial variable x_5 to our problem. The objective function becomes

$$x_1 + 2x_2 + 3x_3 + 0x_4 - wx_5$$

where w is a sufficiently large positive number. The constraints become

$$x_1 + x_2 \qquad \qquad = 5$$
$$x_2 + x_3 + x_4 \qquad = 6$$
$$x_2 - x_3 \qquad + x_5 = 2$$

In this form the first, fourth, and fifth columns of B are the columns of I_3, respectively, and $(x_1,x_2,x_3,x_4,x_5) = (5,0,0,6,2)$ is a basic feasible solution. That it is an extreme solution is left as an exercise.

Thus, after adjoining all necessary slack and artificial variables, the linear programming problem has the form given in (1) to (3), with the added advantage of having an obvious basic feasible solution. For this basic feasible solution the objective function can hardly be expected to attain its maximum. In our example $f(5,0,0,6,2) = 5 - 2w$.

The next step after having found a basic feasible solution is to find one for which the objective function is larger. Instead of working with the variables themselves, we shall work with the corresponding column vectors of B. Since we will use mainly the columns of B, we shall drop the c from our notation for column vectors and simply use β_i to denote β_{ci}^T. It is desired to replace one of the ϵ_i^T by one of the other columns β_k such that (1) and (2) will remain satisfied and f will increase. This process is called "bringing β_k into the basis."

By renumbering the columns of B and the corresponding x_i, we may assume for the first m columns of B that $\beta_i = \epsilon_i^T$ ($i = 1$, ...,m). Then we have $\beta_k - \sum_{i=1}^m b_{ik}\beta_i = \epsilon_0^T$ ($m < k \leq n$), and adding y times this identity to $\sum_{i=1}^m x_i\beta_i = C$, we obtain $y\beta_k + \sum_{i=1}^m (x_i - yb_{ik})\beta_i = C$. For this to be a feasible solution requires $y \geq 0$. The corresponding value of f is $f' = a_k y + \sum_{i=1}^m a_i(x_i - yb_{ik})$. Let $f = \sum_{i=1}^m a_i x_i$ be the value for the old solution and let $f_k = \sum_{i=1}^m a_i b_{ik}$; then $f' = f - y(f_k - a_k)$. Thus, to make $f' > f$, the choice of k for $y > 0$ must be such that $g_k = f_k - a_k < 0$. If there is no negative g_k, no increase is possible and the previous solution is maximal.

In order to obtain the largest increase in the objective function, $-yg_k$ should be as large as possible. However, there are great computational advantages in selecting k such that g_k is the one among the negative g_i's having the largest absolute value.

Before we can bring the corresponding β_k into the basis, we must determine which of the vectors in the basis we wish to remove. In order for the new solution to be feasible, we must have $x_i - yb_{ik} \geq 0$. If $b_{ik} \leq 0$, this is satisfied for any positive y. If $b_{ik} > 0$, it is necessary that $y \leq x_i/b_{ik}$ for all $i \leq m$. Furthermore, the elimination of β_r from the basis requires that $x_r - yb_{rk} = 0$, whence $y = x_r/b_{rk}$. Thus, for the chosen k, we examine the quotients $q_i = x_i/b_{ik}$ and choose r such that q_r is the smallest of the positive q_i's. Since all $x_i \geq 0$, we need consider only the q_i's which correspond to positive b_{ik}'s.

Let us now find the k and r in our example. We write it in the following form:

a_i of Basis	Basis β_i	a_j 0 β_0	1 β_1	2 β_2	3 β_3	0 β_4	$-w$ β_5
1	β_1	5	1	1	0	0	0
0	β_4	6	0	1	1	1	0
$-w$	β_5	2	0	1	-1	0	1
$g_j = \left(\sum_i a_i b_{ij}\right) - a_j$		$5 - 2w$	0	$-w - 1$	$w - 3$	0	0

We have inserted an $a_0 = 0$ such that $g_0 = f$. The basic feasible solution corresponding to this table is $\xi = (5,0,0,6,2)$. Since only $g_2 < 0$, we have $k = 2$. The corresponding q_i are $q_1 = 5$, $q_4 = 6$, and $q_5 = 2$, whence $r = 5$.

In order to remove β_r and introduce β_k, we change the basis by a procedure very similar to Gaussian Elimination. Since we want to make $\beta_{rk} = 1$ and $\beta_{ik} = 0$ ($i \neq r$), we divide the rth row by $b_{rk} > 0$, thus obtaining $b'_{rk} = 1$; then we add $-b_{ik}$ times the new rth row to the ith row for all $i \neq r$ and obtain $b'_{rk} = 0$ ($i \neq r$).

In this manner we obtain a new basic feasible solution, and after a finite number of steps all the g_j will be positive and no further increase in f will be possible.

Substituting β_2 for β_5 in the basis of our example, we get the following table:

a_i of Basis	Basis β_i	a_j 0 β_0	1 β_1	2 β_2	3 β_3	0 β_4	$-w$ β_5
1	β_1	3	1	0	1	0	-1
0	β_4	4	0	0	2	1	-1
2	β_2	2	0	1	-1	0	1
$g_j = \left(\sum_i a_i b_{ij}\right) - a_j$		7	0	0	-4	0	$w + 1$

The corresponding feasible solution is $\xi = (3,2,0,4,0)$. Again only one g_j is negative, namely g_3, and thus $k = 3$. From this $q_1 = 3$, $q_4 = 2$, and $q_2 < 0$. Thus $r = 4$.

Substituting β_3 for β_4 in the basis results in:

a_i of Basis ＼ a_j ＼ Basis β_i ＼ β_j	0 β_0	1 β_1	2 β_2	3 β_3	0 β_4	$-w$ β_5
1 $\quad \beta_1$	1	1	0	0	$-\frac{1}{2}$	$-\frac{1}{2}$
3 $\quad \beta_3$	2	0	0	1	$\frac{1}{2}$	$-\frac{1}{2}$
2 $\quad \beta_2$	4	0	1	0	$\frac{1}{2}$	$\frac{1}{2}$
$g_j = \left(\sum_i a_i b_{ij}\right) - a_j$	15	0	0	0	2	$w - 1$

Since all the g_j's are positive, we can proceed no further. The solution to our example is $x_1 = 1$, $x_2 = 4$, $x_3 = 2$, and $x_4 = x_5 = 0$, with $f_{\max} = 15$.

We shall not go into the resolution of the many complications which can arise in the course of the simplex procedure. The procedure as described above will obtain the solution as long as (1) f has a finite maximum, (2) a "tie" does not arise among the g_j's (that is, there is no $g_j = g_k$ $(j \neq k)$), and (3) a tie does not arise among the q_i's.

Exercise 6.1. Maximize $f = 38x_1 + 4x_2 - 5x_3 + 8x_4$ subject to the constraints $x_i \geq 0$ and

$$
\begin{aligned}
5x_1 + 7x_2 - x_3 - 2x_4 &= -14 \\
x_1 \qquad\qquad + 2x_4 &= 10 \\
x_1 + 6x_2 \qquad - 4x_4 &\leq 4
\end{aligned}
$$

Exercise 6.2. Maximize $f = x_1 + 5x_2$ subject to the constraints $x_i \geq 0$ and

$$
\begin{aligned}
2x_1 + x_2 &\geq 4 \\
-x_1 + 5x_2 &\leq 20 \\
x_1 - 2x_2 &\leq 4 \\
2x_1 + 3x_2 &\leq 25
\end{aligned}
$$

CHAPTER VII

Polynomials

INTRODUCTION

▶**DEFINITION 7.1.** A *polynomial in x of degree n over* $\mathscr{S}$ is an expression of the form $\sum_{i=0}^{n} a_i x^i$, where the a_i belong to $\mathscr{S}$, $a_n \neq 0$, n is a nonnegative integer, and x is a literal commutative with the elements of $\mathscr{S}$ and obeying the laws of exponents.

We shall denote a polynomial in x of degree n by $P(n,x)$. For simplicity we shall frequently write $P(x)$.

For reference purposes, the following theorems from elementary algebra are stated in our nomenclature.

▶**THEOREM 7.1.** Two polynomials in x over $\mathscr{S}$, $P_1(n,x) = \sum_{i=0}^{n} a_i x^i$ and $P_2(m,x) = \sum_{i=0}^{m} b_i x^i$, are equal if and only if $m = n$ and $a_i = b_i$ $(i = 0, \ldots, n)$.

▶**THEOREM 7.2.** Ordinary algebraic addition and multiplication are operations on the set of all polynomials in x over $\mathscr{S}$.

▶**THEOREM 7.3.** The polynomials in x of degree 0 over $\mathscr{S}$ combine like the scalars of $\mathscr{S}$ with respect to addition and multiplication.

▶**THEOREM 7.4.** The division of one polynomial by another polynomial yields a unique quotient and remainder, the degree of the remainder being less than the degree of the divisor.

▶**THEOREM 7.5.** *The Remainder Theorem.* The remainder obtained upon dividing the polynomial $P(x)$ by $(x - a)$ is equal to $P(a)$.

▶**THEOREM 7.6.** *The Factor Theorem.* If $P(a) = 0$, the polynomial $P(x)$ has the factor $(x - a)$.

▶**THEOREM 7.7.** *Rational Roots.* If a polynomial equation over $\mathscr{R}$ with integral coefficients $a_n x^n + a_{n-1} x^{n-1} + \ldots + a_1 x + a_0 = 0$ has the rational root p/q, with p and q integers having no common factor other than unity, then p is an exact divisor of a_0 and q is an exact divisor of a_n.

▶**THEOREM 7.8.** If $P(n,x)$ is a polynomial over $\mathscr{R}^{\#}$, then the roots of $P(n,x) = 0$ which are not in $\mathscr{R}^{\#}$ are conjugate pairs of elements in $\mathscr{C}$.

In addition to these theorems we shall state without proof the Fundamental Theorem of Algebra and a corollary.

▶**THEOREM 7.9.** Every $P(n,x) = 0$ over $\mathscr{C}$ $(n > 0)$ has at least one root in $\mathscr{C}$.

▶**COROLLARY.** Every $P(n,x) = 0$ over $\mathscr{C}$ has exactly n, not necessarily distinct, roots in $\mathscr{C}$.

Exercise 7.1. In the system of Theorem 7.2 find the additive and multiplicative identity elements.

Exercise 7.2. In the set of all polynomials over $\mathscr{R}^{\#}$
   a. Which polynomials have additive inverses?
   b. Which polynomials have multiplicative inverses?

HIGHEST COMMON FACTOR

▶**DEFINITION 7.2.** A common factor of two polynomials $A(x)$ and $B(x)$ is a polynomial which divides both $A(x)$ and $B(x)$.

▶**DEFINITION 7.3.** $G(x)$ is a highest common factor (H.C.F.) of two polynomials $A(x)$ and $B(x)$ if it possesses the following two properties:

(1) $G(x)$ is a common factor of $A(x)$ and $B(x)$; (2) if $C(x)$ is any common factor of $A(x)$ and $B(x)$, then $C(x)$ divides $G(x)$.

To find the H.C.F. of two polynomials, we apply the Euclidean Algorithm to polynomials. Let $F_1(x)$ and $F_2(x)$ ($F_2 \neq 0$, i.e., not the additive identity for polynomials) be two polynomials in x such that the degree of F_1 is equal to or greater than that of F_2. If $Q_1(x)$ is the quotient and $F_3(x)$ is the remainder obtained when F_1 is divided by F_2, then we have the identity

$$F_1 \equiv Q_1 F_2 + F_3 \tag{1}$$

or

$$F_3 \equiv F_1 - Q_1 F_2 \tag{2}$$

If $F_3 \neq 0$, we divide F_2 by F_3, obtaining a quotient Q_2 and a remainder F_4 so that $F_2 \equiv Q_2 F_3 + F_4$. And again, if $F_4 \neq 0$, the division of F_3 by F_4 leads to the identity $F_3 \equiv Q_3 F_4 + F_5$. Since by Theorem 7.4 the degree of F_j is less than that of F_{j-1}, ($j = 3,4,5,\ldots$), continuation in this manner must ultimately lead to a remainder of 0 degree. Thus we have

$$F_1 \equiv Q_1 F_2 + F_3$$
$$F_2 \equiv Q_2 F_3 + F_4$$
$$F_3 \equiv Q_3 F_4 + F_5$$
$$\cdot$$
$$\cdot \tag{3}$$
$$\cdot$$
$$F_{i-2} \equiv Q_{i-2} F_{i-1} + F_i$$
$$F_{i-1} \equiv Q_{i-1} F_i + C(0,x)$$

Two possibilities exist: Either $C \equiv 0$ or $C \not\equiv 0$. Consider first the case $C \not\equiv 0$. Assume F_1 and F_2 have a common polynomial factor $D(x)$ of degree greater than 0. Then from (2), $D(x)$ is obviously a factor of F_3. Similarly, since $D(x)$ is a factor of F_2 and F_3, it is also a factor of F_4, and since $D(x)$ is a factor of F_3 and F_4, it is a factor of F_5. Finally, since $D(x)$ is a factor of F_{i-1} and F_i, it is a factor of C. But this is impossible since C is a constant and $D(x)$ is a polynomial in x of degree greater than 0. Therefore F_1 and F_2 have no common factor containing x if $C \not\equiv 0$, and we say that F_1 and F_2 are *relatively prime* polynomials.

Now if we consider the case in identities (3) with $C \equiv 0$, we have $F_{i-1} \equiv Q_{i-1}F_i$, from which it is clear that F_i is a factor of F_{i-1}. Using this information and going back to the identity $F_{i-2} \equiv Q_{i-2}F_{i-1} + F_i$, we see that F_i is a factor of F_{i-2}. Continuing to work back through identities (3) in this manner, we see that F_i is a factor of both F_2 and F_1. Now to show that F_i is a H.C.F. of F_1 and F_2, let $D(x)$ be any common factor of F_1 and F_2. From identity (2), D is also a factor of F_3. Similarly, working down through the identities in (3) we find that D is a factor of F_4, F_5, . . . , F_{i-2}, and F_{i-1}. Then from $F_i \equiv F_{i-2} - Q_{i-2}F_{i-1}$, D is obviously a factor of F_i. Now since F_i is a factor of both F_1 and F_2 and since any common factor D of F_1 and F_2 is also a factor of F_i, then F_i is a H.C.F. of F_1 and F_2 by definition.

From the identity $F_{i-1} \equiv Q_{i-1}F_i$ it is clear that kF_i (k any nonzero scalar) is also a factor of F_{i-1} and hence, by the same argument that was used to show that F_i is a H.C.F. of F_1 and F_2, it can be shown that kF_i is also a H.C.F. of F_1 and F_2. Thus if F_1 and F_2 have a common factor, then they have many highest common factors, all of which are of the form kF_i, where k is an arbitrary nonzero scalar.

From the standpoint of divisibility, polynomials differing only by a scalar factor may not be considered essentially different. From this viewpoint there is an essentially unique H.C.F. of two polynomials. This unique H.C.F. could be chosen as F_i from the above process or as kF_i with the scalar k so chosen as to obtain a convenient form.

For example, let us use Euclid's Algorithm to find a H.C.F. of the two polynomials over $\mathscr{R}$: (a) $x^4 + x^3 + 2x^2 + x + 1$

and (b) $x^3 - x^2 + x - 1$. We first divide (a) by (b) and obtain a remainder of degree 2.

$$
\begin{array}{r|ll}
x^3 - x^2 + x - 1\big| & x^4 + x^3 + 2x^2 + x + 1 & \big|\underline{x + 2} \\
 & \underline{x^4 - x^3 + x^2 - x} \\
 & 2x^3 + x^2 + 2x + 1 \\
 & \underline{2x^3 - 2x^2 + 2x - 2} \\
 & 3x^2 + 3
\end{array}
$$

Now if we divide $x^3 - x^2 + x - 1$ by $3x^2 + 3$, we encounter fractions. To avoid this minor difficulty, we simply divide the divisor by 3, since such a division can at most change the H.C.F. by a scalar factor, and as pointed out above, this is not an essential change. We then have

$$
\begin{array}{r|ll}
x^2 + 1\big| & x^3 - x^2 + x - 1 & \big|\underline{x - 1} \\
 & \underline{x^3 + x} \\
 & - x^2 - 1 \\
 & \underline{- x^2 - 1}
\end{array}
$$

Thus $x^2 + 1$ corresponds to the function F_i in the general discussion given above, and a H.C.F. for the polynomials (a) and (b) is $x^2 + 1$.

Exercise 7.3. Find a H.C.F. of the following pairs of polynomials over $\mathscr{R}$.

    a. $x^4 - 1$ and $x^5 + x^4 + x^3 + x^2 + x + 1$.
    b. $x^3 - 2x + 1$ and $x^5 + 2x^4 - x^3 - 3x^2 + 1$.
    c. $x^4 + 3x - 2$ and $x^6 + x^4 + 3x^3 - 2x^2 + 3x - 2$.
    d. $x^3 - 2x + 1$ and $x^4 + 3x - 2$.

MULTIPLE ROOTS

According to Theorems 7.6 and 7.9, $P(n,x) = \sum\limits_{i=0}^{n} a_i x^i = a_n \prod\limits_{i=1}^{n} (x - r_i)$. If $P(n,x) = 0$ has multiple roots, we can write

$$
P(n,x) = a_n \prod_{i=1}^{k} (x - r_i)^{\mu_i}, \text{ where } \sum_{i=1}^{k} \mu_i = n \tag{4}
$$

That is, r_i is a root of multiplicity μ_i ($\mu_i \geq 1$). If $\mu_i = 1$, r_i is called a simple root of $P(n,x) = 0$. Upon differentiation of (4) we obtain:

$$\frac{dP(n,x)}{dx} = P'(n,x) = \sum_{i=1}^{n} ia_i x^{i-1} = \left[\prod_{i=1}^{k} (x - r_i)^{\mu_i - 1} \right] Q(k - 1, x)$$

(5)

where no r_i ($i = 1,2,3,\ldots,k$) is a root of $Q(k - 1,x) = 0$. Hence $\prod_{i=1}^{k} (x - r_i)^{\mu_i - 1}$ is a H.C.F. of $P(n,x)$ and $P'(n,x)$.

Thus if we find a H.C.F. of $P(n,x)$ and $P'(n,x)$ by the Euclidean Algorithm and divide $P(n,x)$ by the H.C.F., we obtain a polynomial $R(k,x)$ such that $R = 0$ has each of the r_i as a simple root. Therefore in subsequent discussions we shall be concerned only with polynomial equations having simple roots. For having found the simple roots of $R = 0$, it is a relatively easy matter to determine the multiplicity of each in $P(n,x) = 0$ by synthetic division.*

Furthermore, we shall assume that all rational roots of the polynomial equation have been determined by the use of Theorem 7.7. To simplify our work as much as possible, each time we find a root r of $P(n,x) = 0$, we shall divide $P(n,x)$ by $(x - r)$ and continue with the resulting $P(n - 1,x) = 0$.

The following two theorems for polynomials over $\mathcal{R}$ depend upon the continuity of polynomials. (The proofs are left as exercises.)

▶**THEOREM 7.10.** If $P(n,x_1)$ and $P(n,x_2)$ differ in sign, then $P(n,x) = 0$ has at least one root located between x_1 and x_2.

▶**COROLLARY.** If in the polynomial $P(n,x) = \sum_{i=0}^{n} a_i x^i$, a_0 and a_n differ in sign, then $P(n,x) = 0$ has at least one positive root.

---

* When one works with numerical approximations to j significant figures, roots which do not differ in the first j significant figures will appear as equal roots whether they are actually equal or not.

▶ **THEOREM 7.11.** If in $P(n,x) = \sum\limits_{i=0}^{n} a_i x^i$, all of the nonzero a_i have the same sign, then $P(n,x) = 0$ has no positive roots.

In considering the negative roots of $P(n,x) = 0$, we make use of the fact that if x_j is a root of $P(n,x) = 0$ then $-x_j$ is a root of $P(n,-x) = 0$.

METHODS FOR DETERMINING ROOTS

The student is familiar with methods for finding the roots of polynomial equations of first and second degree in terms of the coefficients. Similarly, such methods exist for polynomial equations of degree three and four. (For reference see any text on the theory of equations.) However, Niels H. Abel (1802–1829) proved that it is impossible to determine the roots of the general polynomial equation of degree five or greater in terms of the coefficients. We shall now consider two of many possible methods for finding approximations to roots of polynomial equations having real coefficients.

INTERVAL-HALVING METHOD

This method uses Theorem 7.10 and the following fact repeatedly. If $x_1 < r < x_2$, then one of the following three conditions prevails:

(1) $x_1 < r < \dfrac{x_1 + x_2}{2}$

(2) $r = \dfrac{x_1 + x_2}{2}$

(3) $\dfrac{x_1 + x_2}{2} < r < x_2$

Suppose that we have given $P(n,x)$ with x_{10} and x_{20}, two distinct values of x, such that $P(x_{10})$ and $P(x_{20})$ differ in sign. Then by Theorem 7.10 $P(x) = 0$ has at least one root between

x_{10} and x_{20}, and we begin our process by evaluating $P\left(\dfrac{x_{10} + x_{20}}{2}\right)$.
If $P\left(\dfrac{x_{10} + x_{20}}{2}\right) = 0$, then $r = \dfrac{x_{10} + x_{20}}{2}$ is a root of $P(x) = 0$.
If $P\left(\dfrac{x_{10} + x_{20}}{2}\right) \neq 0$, then its sign is opposite to the sign of either $P(x_{10})$ or $P(x_{20})$. Thus we have found a new pair of values x_{11} and x_{21} to which Theorem 7.10 applies.

Repeating this process i times, we obtain a pair of values x_{1i} and x_{2i} for which $P(x_{1i})$ and $P(x_{2i})$ differ in sign. The root of $P(x) = 0$ which is located between x_{1i} and x_{2i} is equal to $\dfrac{x_{1i} + x_{2i}}{2} \pm \epsilon$, where $0 \leq \epsilon < \left|\dfrac{x_{2i} - x_{1i}}{2}\right|$. Hence if we use $\dfrac{x_{1i} + x_{2i}}{2}$ as an approximation for r, we have an error less than $\left|\dfrac{x_{2i} - x_{1i}}{2}\right|$. In order to determine the number of times to apply the process to obtain a prescribed degree of accuracy, observe that $\epsilon < \left|\dfrac{x_{20} - x_{10}}{2^i}\right|$. Thus if δ is the maximum error to be tolerated, we can determine the number of iterations by solving for the least integral value of i satisfying $\left|\dfrac{x_{20} - x_{10}}{2^i}\right| \leq \delta$. Since this method depends only on continuity, it is not restricted to polynomials alone but can be used to determine 0's of any continuous function.

Exercise 7.4. Find the real root of $x^3 + 9x - 2 = 0$.
Exercise 7.5. Find the real root of $x^3 + 6x + 2 = 0$.

QUADRATIC FACTORING METHOD

Since the interval-halving method is restricted to determining real roots only, we now present a method by which complex, as well as real, roots of polynomial equations can be determined.

Essentially the method consists of successive synthetic divisions by quadratic factors.

Given the polynomial $P(n,x) = \sum_{i=0}^{n} a_i x^{n-i}$ and dividing by the quadratic $(x^2 + px + q)$, we obtain a quotient $\sum_{i=0}^{n-2} b_i x^{n-i-2}$ and a remainder $rx + s$ or

$$P(n,x) = a_0 x^n + a_1 x^{n-1} + \ldots + a_{n-1} x + a_n$$
$$= (x^2 + px + q)(b_0 x^{n-2} + b_1 x^{n-3}$$
$$+ \ldots + b_{n-3} x + b_{n-2}) + rx + s$$

Equating corresponding coefficients, we have

$$
\begin{aligned}
a_0 &= b_0 \\
a_1 &= b_1 + pb_0 \\
a_2 &= b_2 + pb_1 + qb_0 \\
&\cdot \qquad \cdot \\
&\cdot \qquad \cdot \\
&\cdot \qquad \cdot \\
a_{n-2} &= b_{n-2} + pb_{n-3} + qb_{n-4} \\
a_{n-1} &= r + pb_{n-2} + qb_{n-3} \\
a_n &= s + qb_{n-2}
\end{aligned}
\tag{6}
$$

If we define

$$
\begin{aligned}
b_{-2} &= b_{-1} = 0 \\
r &= b_{n-1} \\
s &= b_n + pb_{n-1}
\end{aligned}
\tag{7}
$$

we can write

$$a_i = b_i + pb_{i-1} + qb_{i-2} \ (i = 0,1, \ldots, n)$$

Solving for b_i, we obtain the recursion formula

$$b_i = a_i - pb_{i-1} - qb_{i-2} \ (i = 0,1, \ldots, n) \tag{8}$$

which enables us to compute the b_i's successively from the a_i's, p, and q.

We would like to find a value of p and a value of q such that division of $P(x)$ by $x^2 + px + q$ gives a 0 remainder. If an arbitrary choice of p and q does not produce the desired 0 remainder, then the problem is to determine what changes in p and q (Δp and Δq) yield a remainder nearer 0. From (7) we have

$$r = b_{n-1}$$
$$s = b_n + pb_{n-1} \tag{9}$$

Since the a's are constants and the b's are functions of the two independent variables p and q, it follows that

$$\Delta r = \frac{\partial b_{n-1}}{\partial p} \Delta p + \frac{\partial b_{n-1}}{\partial q} \Delta q$$

and

$$\Delta s = \left[\frac{\partial b_n}{\partial p} + b_{n-1} + p \frac{\partial b_{n-1}}{\partial p} \right] \Delta p + \left[\frac{\partial b_n}{\partial q} + p \frac{\partial b_{n-1}}{\partial q} \right] \Delta q \tag{10}$$

Since $(r + \Delta r)$ and $(s + \Delta s)$ are approximately the coefficients of the remainder when $P(x)$ is divided by $x^2 + (p + \Delta p)x + (q + \Delta q)$, we set $(r + \Delta r) = (s + \Delta s) = 0$. Thus we have

$$r + \Delta r = b_{n-1} + \frac{\partial b_{n-1}}{\partial p} \Delta p + \frac{\partial b_{n-1}}{\partial q} \Delta q = 0 \tag{11}$$

and

$$s + \Delta s = b_n + pb_{n-1} + \left[\frac{\partial b_n}{\partial p} + b_{n-1} + p \frac{\partial b_{n-1}}{\partial p} \right] \Delta p$$

$$+ \left[\frac{\partial b_n}{\partial q} + \frac{p \partial b_{n-1}}{\partial q} \right] \Delta q = 0 \tag{12}$$

From (11) and (12) we obtain

$$-\frac{\partial b_{n-1}}{\partial p} \Delta p - \frac{\partial b_{n-1}}{\partial q} \Delta q = b_{n-1}$$

and

$$-\left(\frac{\partial b_n}{\partial p} + b_{n-1} \right) \Delta p - \frac{\partial b_n}{\partial q} \Delta q = b_n \tag{13}$$

Now if we differentiate (8) with respect to p and q, respectively, we obtain

$$\frac{\partial b_i}{\partial p} = -b_{i-1} - p\frac{\partial b_{i-1}}{\partial p} - q\frac{\partial b_{i-2}}{\partial p} \tag{14}$$

and

$$\frac{\partial b_i}{\partial q} = -b_{i-2} - p\frac{\partial b_{i-1}}{\partial q} - q\frac{\partial b_{i-2}}{\partial q} \tag{15}$$

Let us introduce the recursion formula [similar to (8)]:

$$\begin{aligned} c_{-1} &= 0 \\ c_0 &= a_0 \\ c_k &= b_k - pc_{k-1} - qc_{k-2} \ (k = 1, 2, \ldots, n-1) \end{aligned} \tag{16}$$

This, together with (14) and (15), gives

$$\begin{aligned} \frac{\partial b_k}{\partial p} &= -c_{k-1} \\ \frac{\partial b_k}{\partial q} &= -c_{k-2} \end{aligned} \tag{17}$$

for $k = 1, 2, \ldots, n$. Substituting (17) in (13), we have

$$\begin{aligned} c_{n-2}\,\Delta p + c_{n-3}\,\Delta q &= b_{n-1} \\ (c_{n-1} - b_{n-1})\,\Delta p + c_{n-2}\,\Delta q &= b_n \end{aligned} \tag{18}$$

or

$$\begin{aligned} c_{n-2}\,\Delta p + c_{n-3}\,\Delta q &= b_{n-1} \\ c\,\Delta p + c_{n-2}\,\Delta q &= b_n \end{aligned} \tag{19}$$

where

$$c = c_{n-1} - b_{n-1} = -pc_{n-2} - qc_{n-3} \tag{20}$$

By means of the recursion formula, we can compute the c_i's and c from the b_i's, p, and q. The next step is to solve equations (19) simultaneously to obtain

$$\begin{aligned} \Delta p &= \frac{b_{n-1}c_{n-2} - b_n c_{n-3}}{c_{n-2}^2 - cc_{n-3}} = \frac{\text{Num. } \Delta p}{\text{Denom.}} \\ \Delta q &= \frac{-b_{n-1}c + b_n c_{n-2}}{c_{n-2}^2 - cc_{n-3}} = \frac{\text{Num. } \Delta q}{\text{Denom.}} \end{aligned} \tag{21}$$

Then we use $(p + \Delta p)$ and $(q + \Delta q)$ as new coefficients in the quadratic and repeat the process until we obtain the desired accuracy for p and q.

For example, let us find all of the roots of $x^4 + 3x^3 + 3x^2 - 6x - 10 = 0$ to three significant figures. We first ascertain that there are no multiple or rational roots. Then beginning with $p = q = 0$ and using recursion formulas (8) and (16), we obtain

$$
\begin{aligned}
b_0 &= 1 & c_0 &= 1 \\
b_1 &= 3 & c_1 &= 3 \\
b_2 &= 3 & c_2 &= 3 \\
b_3 &= -6 & c_3 &= -6 \\
b_4 &= -10 &&
\end{aligned}
$$

From (20) we compute $c = -6 - (-6) = 0$. From (21) we obtain

Num. $\Delta p = b_3c_2 - b_4c_1 \quad = (-6)(3) - (-10)(3) = 12$

Num. $\Delta q = -b_3c + b_4c_2 = 6(0) + (-10)(3) \quad = -30$

Denom. $= c_2{}^2 - cc_1 \quad = 3^2 - 0(3) \quad = 9$

from which

$$\Delta p = \frac{12}{9} \quad = 1.33,$$

$$\Delta q = \frac{-30}{9} = -3.33$$

Since we let $p = q = 0$ initially, we have for the second iteration

$$p = 0 + 1.33 = 1.33$$
$$q = 0 - 3.33 = -3.33$$

Continuing through five iterations in the same manner as above, we find the results which are given in Table 7.1.

We note from the table that $\Delta p = \Delta q = 0$, to the desired accuracy, in the fifth iteration. Hence we terminate the process

Table 7.1

Iterations		I		II		III		IV		V	
p	q	0.00	0.00	1.33	−3.33	0.45	−2.70	0.06	−2.08	0.00	−2.00
i	a_i	b_i	c_i	b_i	c_i	b_i	c_i	b_i	c_i	b_i	c_i
0	1.00	1.00	1.00	1.00	1.00	1.00	1.00	1.00	1.00	1.00	1.00
1	3.00	3.00	3.00	1.67	0.34	2.55	2.10	2.94	2.88	3.00	3.00
2	3.00	3.00	3.00	4.11	6.99	4.55	6.30	4.90	6.81	5.00	7.00
3	−6.00	−6.00	†	−5.91		−1.16		−0.17		0.00	
4	−10.00	−10.00	0.00*	11.55	−8.17	2.81	2.83	0.20	5.58	0.00	6.00
Denom.		9.00		51.64		33.75		30.31		31 00	
Num. $\Delta p, \Delta q$		12.00	−30.00	−45.24	32.45	−13.21	20.98	−1.74	2.31	0.00	0.00
$\Delta p, \Delta q$		1.33	−3.33	−0.88	0.63	−0.39	0.62	−0.06	0.08	0.00	0.00

† Since c is computed from c_{n-2} and c_{n-3} by (20), c_{n-1} is never used, and we shall omit its computation.
* Since there is no c_n, we shall put c in this position.

with the values $p = 0$ and $q = -2$. Thus $x^2 - 2$ is one of the desired factors of $x^4 + 3x^3 + 3x^2 - 6x - 10 = 0$. By division we obtain the remaining quadratic factor $x^2 + 3x + 5$. From the quadratic factors we obtain the required roots ± 1.41 and $-1.50 \pm 1.66i$. For polynomial equations of degree greater than four, the second factor would be of degree greater than two and the entire process outlined above would be repeated on this factor to obtain a second quadratic factor, etc.

Exercise 7.6. Starting with $p = q = 0$, find one quadratic factor of $x^4 - 8x^3 + 39x^2 - 62x + 50 = 0$. (Use three significant figures in the computation.)

CHAPTER VIII

Groups

INTRODUCTION

In the previous chapters we defined several mathematical systems as we needed them. In this and the following three chapters we shall give a more systematic development of such mathematical systems, beginning with a relatively simple system having only one operation and progressing to a system having three operations.

▶**DEFINITION 8.1.** A *group* $\mathscr{G}$ is a system consisting of a set G of elements, a closed binary operation $\bigcirc$, and the following postulates:

(1) $\bigcirc$ is associative on G.
(2) There exists an identity element e in G for the operation $\bigcirc$.
(3) For every element in G there exists in G an inverse with respect to $\bigcirc$.

▶**DEFINITION 8.2.** An *Abelian group* (commutative group) is a group with the additional postulate:

(4) $\bigcirc$ is commutative on G.

For example, the set of all even integers under addition forms an Abelian group. Addition is an operation on the set because the sum of two even integers is an even integer. Postulates (1) and (4) are satisfied since addition is associative and commutative on $\mathscr{R}^{\#}$. Since 0 (an even integer) is the unique additive identity, postulate (2) is satisfied. Postulate (3) is satisfied since for every even integer a the additive inverse $-a$ is also an even integer.

As a second example, consider the set of $n \times n$ matrices under matrix multiplication. This system does not form a group since postulate (3) is not satisfied for any singular matrix. However, if we restrict our discussion to the set of all nonsingular $n \times n$ matrices, we have a non-Abelian group. The verification of this is left as an exercise.

Exercise 8.1. Which of the following systems are groups? For those systems which are not groups, show which conditions of the definition are not satisfied.

    a. All odd integers under addition.
    b. All odd integers under multiplication.
    c. All even integers under multiplication.
    d. All integers with $a \bigcirc b = a - b$.
    e. All integral multiples of 3 under addition.
    f. All $m \times n$ matrices with integral elements under addition.
    g. All $n \times n$ nonsingular matrices with rational elements under addition.
    h. The set of all third order vectors (a,b,c) over $\mathscr{R}$ with $ac \neq 0$, where $(a_1,b_1,c_1) \bigcirc (a_2,b_2,c_2) = (a_1 a_2, a_1 b_2 + b_1 c_2, c_1 c_2)$.

Exercise 8.2. Which of the groups in Exercise 8.1 are Abelian?

Exercise 8.3. Show that a system of vectors is an Abelian group.

Exercise 8.4. For a group $\mathscr{G}$,
    a. Show that the identity is unique.
    b. Show that the inverse is unique.
    c. Show that the inverse of the inverse of a is a.

FINITE GROUPS

▶**DEFINITION 8.3.** A group $\mathscr{G}$ for which G is a finite set is a *finite group*.

For an example of a finite group, consider the set of congruences of an equilateral triangle. In general, a congruence of a regular polygon is the rigid motion (in space) of the polygon into itself.

Thus for the equilateral triangle in Figure 8.1, the six congruences are three semirotations L_1, L_2, and L_3 about the lines L_1, L_2, and L_3, respectively, and the three rotations R, R^2, and R^3 of 120°, 240°, and 360°, respectively, about C. Let the operation be called "product," and by analogy to the product

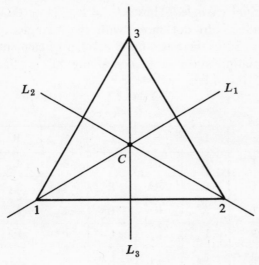

Figure 8.1.

of linear transformations, define the product AB of two congruences A and B to be the motion A followed by the motion B. Since rotation R followed by itself is a rotation through 240°, we have $RR = R^2$. (This explains our choice of notation.)

Consider the product RL_1. Now R applied to the original triangle produces

and L_1 applied to this triangle produces

This result could have been obtained directly by applying L_2 to the original triangle. Thus $RL_1 = L_2$. Note that the lines L_1, L_2, and L_3 do not move with the triangle. Similarly, $L_1L_2 = R^2$. Since there is a finite number of elements, we can write a multiplication table containing all of the possible products (Table 8.1.).

TABLE 8.1

Right Factor

	L_1	L_2	L_3	R	R^2	R^3
L_1	R^3	R^2	R	L_2	L_3	L_1
L_2	R	R^3	R^2	L_3	L_1	L_2
L_3	R^2	R	R^3	L_1	L_2	L_3
R	L_3	L_1	L_2	R^2	R^3	R
R^2	L_2	L_3	L_1	R^3	R	R^2
R^3	L_1	L_2	L_3	R	R^2	R^3

Left Factor

From Table 8.1 we see that "product" is an operation. Furthermore, R^3 is the identity element satisfying postulate (2), the inverse of L_i is L_i ($i = 1,2,3$), R and R^2 are inverses of each other, and R^3 is its own inverse. The verification of postulate (1) is left as an exercise. Thus this set of congruences forms a group. That the group is non-Abelian is apparent from Table 8.1. For instance, $RL_1 \neq L_1R$.

Exercise 8.5. Show that the following are finite Abelian groups and write the group table for each.

   a. ± 1 and $\pm i$ under multiplication.
   b. 1, ω, ω^2 under multiplication ($\omega^3 = 1$).

c. The six complex numbers $e^{(ik\pi/3)} = \cos\dfrac{k\pi}{3} + i\sin\dfrac{k\pi}{3}$ $(k = 0,$ $1, \ldots, 5)$ under multiplication.

d. The congruences of a square under "product."

e. The following six matrices under multiplication:

$$A_1 = \begin{pmatrix} 0 & 1 & 0 \\ 1 & 0 & 0 \\ 0 & 0 & 1 \end{pmatrix} \quad A_2 = \begin{pmatrix} 0 & 0 & 1 \\ 0 & 1 & 0 \\ 1 & 0 & 0 \end{pmatrix} \quad A_3 = \begin{pmatrix} 1 & 0 & 0 \\ 0 & 0 & 1 \\ 0 & 1 & 0 \end{pmatrix}$$

$$A_4 = \begin{pmatrix} 0 & 1 & 0 \\ 0 & 0 & 1 \\ 1 & 0 & 0 \end{pmatrix} \quad A_5 = \begin{pmatrix} 0 & 0 & 1 \\ 1 & 0 & 0 \\ 0 & 1 & 0 \end{pmatrix} \quad A_6 = \begin{pmatrix} 1 & 0 & 0 \\ 0 & 1 & 0 \\ 0 & 0 & 1 \end{pmatrix}$$

Exercise 8.6. Does there exist a group with only one element?

SUBGROUPS

We shall arbitrarily adopt the language of multiplication for the group operation. Under this convention the identity element will be written as 1. We shall not hestitate to make exceptions to this procedure when there is a more conventional system of notation. For example, in the group of even integers under addition we shall use $+$ for the operation and 0 for the identity element.

▶**DEFINITION 8.4.** The *order* of a finite group $\mathscr{G}$ is the number of elements in G.

▶**DEFINITION 8.5.** A subsystem of a group $\mathscr{G}$, which is a group with respect to the operation of $\mathscr{G}$, is a *subgroup* of $\mathscr{G}$.

▶**THEOREM 8.1.** Necessary and sufficient conditions that a subsystem $\mathscr{H}$ of a group $\mathscr{G}$ be a subgroup are:

(1) The operation on G is an operation on H.

(2) For every element in H, the inverse is in H.

PROOF: The necessity is obvious, for if $\mathscr{H}$ is a group these conditions are satisfied. To show the sufficiency we observe that condition (1) establishes the existence of the operation and that condition (2) is postulate (3) of Definition 8.1. Postulate (1) is satisfied since the operation is associative on G. Postulate (2) is satisfied since by condition (2) an element and its inverse are both in H and by condition (1) their product, the identity element, is in H. Thus all of the postulates are satisfied and $\mathscr{H}$ is a subgroup of $\mathscr{G}$.

▶**THEOREM 8.2.** The order of a finite group $\mathscr{G}$ is a multiple of the order of any of its subgroups.

PROOF: Let $\mathscr{G}$ be of order g and let $\mathscr{H}$ be a subgroup of $\mathscr{G}$ of order h. If $g = h$, the theorem is obvious. Otherwise, let $a_1 = 1, a_2, a_3, \ldots, a_h$ be elements of H. Let b_2 be an element of G not in H. Form the elements $b_2 a_i$ $(i = 1, 2, \ldots, h)$ in G. If this does not exhaust G, choose b_3 in G not among the previous elements. Form the elements $b_3 a_i$ $(i = 1, 2, \ldots, h)$ in G. If necessary, repeat with b_4 not among the previous elements, etc. Since $\mathscr{G}$ is finite, this procedure must, for some b_k, exhaust the elements of G. We have now written hk, not necessarily distinct, elements of G. To facilitate the proof that no two elements are the same, we let $b_1 = 1$. Thus an element a_i of H can be written as $b_1 a_i$.

We shall prove, first, that no two elements formed with the same b_i are equal; second, that no two elements formed with different b_i are equal.

(1) Since b_i is an element of G, it has an inverse b_i^{-1} in G. Thus if $b_i a_m = b_i a_n$, then $b_i^{-1} b_i a_m = b_i^{-1} b_i a_n$ yields $a_m = a_n$. Hence for $a_m \neq a_n$ we have $b_i a_m \neq b_i a_n$.

(2) If $b_i a_m = b_j a_n$, $(j < i)$, postmultiplication by a_m^{-1} gives $b_i a_m a_m^{-1} = b_j a_n a_m^{-1}$, whence $b_i = b_j a_n a_m^{-1}$, which is a contradiction to the choice of b_i. Thus the hk elements are distinct. Since they exhaust G, we have $hk = g$.

▶THEOREM 8.3. In a finite group $\mathscr{G}$, let A be the set containing any element a of G together with its successive powers. The system $\mathscr{A}$ consisting of A and the operation of $\mathscr{G}$ is a subgroup of $\mathscr{G}$.

PROOF: Let the order of the group $\mathscr{G}$ be g. If $a = 1$, the theorem is obvious. Otherwise the set of elements a^i ($i = 1$, $2, \ldots, g + 1$) contains $g + 1$ elements of G. Since G contains exactly g elements, two of the powers of a must be identical. Suppose $a^i = a^j$ ($i < j$). Since $a^{j-i}a^i = a^j = a^i$, we have $a^{j-i} = 1$. Let k be the smallest positive integer such that $a^k = 1$. The set A of elements a^i ($i = 1, 2, \ldots, k$) contains all of the distinct elements a^i since $a^{k+1} = a$, $a^{k+2} = a^2$, etc. The operation of $\mathscr{G}$ is obviously an operation on A. Since for $i \neq k$, $a^{k-i}a^i = a^k = 1$, the inverse of a^i is a^{k-i} and a^k is its own inverse. Thus by Theorem 8.1 $\mathscr{A}$ is a subgroup of $\mathscr{G}$.

▶THEOREM 8.4. In a group $\mathscr{G}$ let A be the set of all a^i ($i = \ldots, -2, -1, 0, 1, 2, \ldots$). The system $\mathscr{A}$ consisting of A and the operation of $\mathscr{G}$ is a subgroup of $\mathscr{G}$.

PROOF: Exercise.

We note that Theorem 8.3 is a special case of Theorem 8.4. The subgroup in these theorems is called the subgroup *generated* by a.

▶DEFINITION 8.6. The *order* of an element of a finite group is the order of the subgroup it generates

As a consequence of Definition 8.6 and Theorem 8.2, we have the following theorem.

▶THEOREM 8.5. The order of a finite group $\mathscr{G}$ is a multiple of the order of any of the elements of G.

As a generalization of the subgroup generated by an element a, we define:

▶**DEFINITION 8.7.** If G contains an element a such that the subgroup generated by a is $\mathscr{G}$, then $\mathscr{G}$ is a *cyclic group* and a is called a *generator* of the group.

By this definition the subgroups in Theorem 8.3 and Theorem 8.4 are cyclic groups.

▶**THEOREM 8.6.** Any cyclic group is Abelian.

PROOF: $a^i a^k = a^{i+k} = a^{k+i} = a^k a^i$.

Exercise 8.7. Find all the subgroups contained in:
  a. The group in Exercise 8.5c.
  b. The group in Exercise 8.5d.
  c. The group in Exercise 8.5e.
  d. The multiplicative group of the six congruences of an equilateral triangle.

Exercise 8.8. For the groups in Exercise 8.7 give the order of each element.

Exercise 8.9. Show that $\mathscr{G}$ is Abelian if and only if $(ab)^2 = a^2 b^2$ for all a and b in G.

Exercise 8.10. If $\mathscr{H}$ and $\mathscr{K}$ are subgroups of a group $\mathscr{G}$, prove that the system consisting of the set of all elements common to both H and K together with the operation of $\mathscr{G}$ is also a subgroup of $\mathscr{G}$.

Exercise 8.11. Is the multiplicative group of congruences of the equilateral triangle cyclic? Why?

Exercise 8.12. Is the group of integers under addition cyclic?

Exercise 8.13. Show that the system consisting of the set of elements $1, -1, i, -i, (i^2 = -1)$ with multiplication is a cyclic group. Which elements are generators?

Exercise 8.14. Prove that the system consisting of the set of the nth roots of unity under multiplication is a cyclic group of order n.

Exercise 8.15. Show that a group whose order is a prime is cyclic.

Exercise 8.16. Show that in a cyclic group whose order is a prime every element except the identity is a generator.

ABSTRACT GROUPS

In the group table for Exercise 8.5e we see that $(A_4)^2 = A_5$ and $(A_4)^3 = A_6$. Letting $A_4 = S$, $A_1 = T$, then in terms of S and T we have $A_1 = T$, $A_2 = S^2T$, $A_3 = ST$, $A_4 = S$, $A_5 = S^2$, and $A_6 = S^3$. The group table becomes Table 8.2.

TABLE 8.2

	T	S²T	ST	S	S²	S³
T	S³	S	S²	S²T	ST	T
S²T	S²	S³	S	ST	T	S²T
ST	S	S²	S³	T	S²T	ST
S	ST	T	S²T	S²	S³	S
S²	S²T	ST	T	S³	S	S²
S³	T	S²T	ST	S	S²	S³

We observe that Table 8.2 is very similar to the group table for congruences of the equilateral triangle (Table 8.1). In fact, if we replaced L_1 by T, L_2 by S^2T, L_3 by ST, and R by S, they would be identical. Although we arrived at these two groups by entirely different procedures, they are fundamentally the same. That is, we have a one-to-one correspondence between the congruences and the matrices. Furthermore, any relation holding among the congruences will hold among the corresponding matrices and vice versa. In particular, the product of any two congruences corresponds to the product of the two corresponding matrices.

▶DEFINITION 8.8. *Isomorphism.* If a set of elements with certain operations is identical (except possibly for notation) to another set and its operations, the two corresponding systems are *isomorphic*.

In particular, for two groups $\mathscr{G}$ and $\mathscr{H}$ to be isomorphic means:

1. There is a one-to-one correspondence between G and H.
2. If a_1, b_1, c_1 in G correspond to a_2, b_2, c_2 in H and $a_1 \, \textcircled{1} \, b_1 = c_1$ in $\mathscr{G}$, then $a_2 \, \textcircled{2} \, b_2 = c_2$ in $\mathscr{H}$.

Thus our previous discussion is a demonstration that the group of congruences of an equilateral triangle is isomorphic to the group represented by Table 8.2. Obviously any group isomorphic to either of the groups represented by Tables 8.1 or 8.2 must be isomorphic to the other. Hence any group isomorphic to these groups must have what is essentially the same group table. Thus Table 8.2 is an abstract representation of any group isomorphic to these groups of order six.

Isomorphism is an equivalence relation on any set of algebraic systems. Verification of this is left as an exercise. An isomorphism leads to equivalence classes of isomorphic algebraic systems. Such an equivalence class will be called an *abstract algebraic system*. Any specific algebraic system contained in the equivalence class may be selected to represent the abstract system.

This discussion leads to the question: Is there more than one abstract group of order six? Or, more generally, how many abstract groups exist for a given order? We shall first show the existence of a group of any order and then consider the existence of additional abstract groups of the same order.

▶**THEOREM 8.7.** There exists a cyclic group for any order.

PROOF: Letting n be any arbitrary positive integer, the system $\mathscr{A}$ consisting of the set of elements $a, a^2, a^3, \ldots, a^{n-1}, a^n = 1$ under multiplication is a cyclic group of order n. Furthermore, the integers under addition form a cyclic group of infinite order.

Our first question has now been answered since Table 8.2 represents a noncyclic group of order six and Theorem 8.7

demonstrates the existence of a cyclic group of the same order. Thus there exist at least two abstract groups of order six. The group in Exercise 8.5c is an example of a cyclic group of order six.

▶**THEOREM 8.8.** Two cyclic groups of the same order are isomorphic.

PROOF: Exercise.

▶**THEOREM 8.9.** If p is a prime, the cyclic group is the only abstract group of order p.

PROOF: A group $\mathscr{G}$ of order p must contain an element a whose order is not 1. Since p is a prime, it follows from Theorem 8.5 that the order of a is p; hence $\mathscr{G}$ is cyclic. The conclusion follows from Theorem 8.8.

▶**COROLLARY.** In a group of prime order p, every non-identity element is of order p and hence generates the group.

We have shown that there is exactly one abstract group of any prime order and that there can be more than one abstract group of composite order. The question of the exact number of abstract groups of a particular composite order must be left unanswered. For some small composite orders the number of groups is as follows:

Order	4	6	8	9	10	12	14	15	16	18
Number	2	2	5	2	2	5	2	1	14	5

The fact that there exists only one abstract group of order fifteen shows that there is not necessarily more than one abstract group of a particular composite order.

Exercise 8.17. Show that an Abelian group cannot be isomorphic to a non-Abelian group.

Exercise 8.18. Construct a group table for each abstract group of order four.

Exercise 8.19. If for every element a of a finite group $\mathscr{G}$, $a^2 = 1$, show:

  a. That $\mathscr{G}$ is an Abelian group.
  b. That the order of $\mathscr{G}$ is 2^k.

Exercise 8.20. Show that the elements of J_m form an Abelian group under addition.

Exercise 8.21. Give the group tables for three nonisomorphic abstract Abelian groups of order eight. (*Hint:* To show they are nonisomorphic, consider the order of each element.)

CHAPTER IX

Rings, Integral Domains, and Fields

RINGS

In Chapter VIII we discussed mathematical systems with one operation. We shall now consider mathematical systems with two operations.

▶DEFINITION 9.1. A *ring* $\mathcal{N}$ is a system consisting of a set N of elements, two operations, ① and ②, and the following postulates:

(1) N with ① is an Abelian group.
(2) ② is associative on N.
(3) ② is left and right distributive with respect to ①.

▶DEFINITION 9.2. A ring $\mathcal{N}$ in which ② is commutative on N is a *commutative ring*.

▶DEFINITION 9.3. If N contains an identity element for ②, $\mathcal{N}$ is a ring with unity.

For example, let N be the set of all 2×2 matrices with integral elements, ① be matrix addition, and ② be matrix multiplication. This system $\mathcal{N}$ is a ring with unity, but is not a commutative ring. That ② is an operation on N follows from the fact that sums and products of integers are integers. That ① is an operation on N and postulate (1) is satisfied are shown in Exercises 8.1 and 8.2. Postulates (2) and (3) are special cases of Theorems 4.4 and 4.5. Furthermore, I_2 is in N. That ② is not commutative on N is easily verified.

As before we shall arbitrarily adopt the language of addition and multiplication for ① and ②, respectively.

▶**THEOREM 9.1.** In a ring with unity the multiplicative identity is unique.

PROOF: Exercise.

▶**THEOREM 9.2.** In a ring $a0 = 0a = 0$.

PROOF: Since the ring is an additive Abelian group, $b + 0 = b$. Premultiplication by a together with postulate (3) gives $ab + a0 = ab$. By the uniqueness of the identity element of a group, $a0 = 0$. Similarly, $0a = 0$.

However, the converse of Theorem 9.2 does not hold. That is, $ab = 0$ does not necessitate a or $b = 0$. For instance, in the above example

$$\begin{pmatrix} 0 & 1 \\ 0 & 0 \end{pmatrix} \quad \begin{pmatrix} 0 & 1 \\ 0 & 0 \end{pmatrix} = \begin{pmatrix} 0 & 0 \\ 0 & 0 \end{pmatrix}$$

▶**DEFINITION 9.4.** If a and b are nonzero elements in a ring $\mathcal{N}$ and either or both of their products is 0, then both a and b are *divisors of 0*.

In the ring of our example $\begin{pmatrix} 0 & 1 \\ 0 & 0 \end{pmatrix}$ is a divisor of 0.

▶**THEOREM 9.3.** The following *cancellation law for multiplication* holds in a commutative ring. If $c \neq 0$ is not a divisor of 0 and $ca = cb$, then $a = b$.

PROOF: If $ca = cb$, then $ca - cb = c(a - b) = 0$. For $c \neq 0$ and not a divisor of 0, $a - b$ must be 0. Hence $a = b$.

Exercise 9.1. Show that the system consisting of the set of all integers with addition and multiplication forms a commutative ring with unity. Show that this ring has no divisors of 0.

Exercise 9.2. Which of the systems consisting of the following sets with addition and multiplication are rings? With unity? Commutative? If not, why not?

a. All matrices of the form $\begin{pmatrix} 0 & a \\ -a & 0 \end{pmatrix}$ over the rationals.

b. The pure imaginary numbers.

c. All polynomials in x with rational coefficients.

d. All $a + b\sqrt{2}$ with a and b integral; rational.

e. $a\sqrt{2}$ with a rational.

f. $a + b\sqrt{2} + c\sqrt{3}$ with a, b, and c rational.

g. $\mathscr{J}_6$.

h. All even integers.

Exercise 9.3. Which of the rings in Exercise 9.2 contain divisors of 0?

Exercise 9.4. Is it possible to have a ring containing only two elements? Verify.

Exercise 9.5. Show that $\mathscr{J}_m$ is a commutative ring with unity.

Exercise 9.6. Show that the system of all polynomials in x over a ring (instead of a system of scalars) is a ring.

Exercise 9.7. Use Exercise 9.6 to define the ring of all polynomials in n variables over $\mathscr{R}^\#$.

INTEGRAL DOMAINS

▶DEFINITION 9.5. An *integral domain* $\mathscr{D}$ is a commutative ring with unity which contains no divisors of 0.

▶DEFINITION 9.5a An *integral domain* $\mathscr{D}$ is a commutative ring with unity in which $c \neq 0$ and $ca = cb$ imply $a = b$.

By virtue of Exercise 9.1 the integers form an integral domain under addition and multiplication.

Exercise 9.8. Prove that Definition 9.5 and Definition 9.5a are equivalent.

Exercise 9.9. Do the rational numbers form an integral domain under addition and multiplication?

Exercise 9.10. Which of the systems in Exercise 9.2 are integral domains?

Exercise 9.11. If $\mathcal{D}$ is an integral domain and a ring $\mathcal{N}$ is a subset of $\mathcal{D}$, is $\mathcal{N}$ necessarily an integral domain?

Exercise 9.12. Show that the set of all $a + ib$, where a and b are integers, forms an integral domain under addition and multiplication.

Exercise 9.13. Show that the system of all matrices of the form $\begin{pmatrix} a & b \\ -b & a \end{pmatrix}$, where a and b are integers, with matrix addition and multiplication is isomorphic to the system of Exercise 9.10, and hence is an integral domain.

Exercise 9.14. Show that the system consisting of the set of all polynomials in x over $\mathcal{D}$ with addition and multiplication of polynomials is an integral domain.

FIELDS

▶**DEFINITION 9.6.** A *field* $\mathcal{F}$ is a commutative ring with unity in which every element except the identity element with respect to ① has an inverse with respect to ②.

▶**DEFINITION 9.6a.** A *field* $\mathcal{F}$ is an integral domain in which every nonzero element has a multiplicative inverse.

▶**DEFINITION 9.6b.** A *field* $\mathcal{F}$ is a set of elements which forms an Abelian group under addition, whose nonzero elements form an Abelian group under multiplication, and in which multiplication is distributive with respect to addition.

Some obvious examples of fields are the system of all rational numbers and the system of all complex numbers.

Note that Definition 1.15 is the definition of a field with all postulates listed in detail. Thus in our early chapters the system of scalars was an arbitrary field, and we defined vectors, matrices, etc., over fields.

Exercise 9.15. Show that Definition 1.15 and Definition 9.6 are equivalent.

Exercise 9.16. Show that Definition 9.6a and Definition 9.6b are equivalent.

Exercise 9.17. With ① as addition and ② as multiplication, show that Definition 9.6 and Definition 9.6a are equivalent.

Exercise 9.18. Which of the systems in Exercise 9.2 are fields?

Exercise 9.19. Show that the set of all matrices of the form $\begin{pmatrix} a & b \\ -b & a \end{pmatrix}$ over $\mathscr{R}^{\#}$ with matrix addition and multiplication is a field.

Exercise 9.20. Is the system of all $n \times n$ matrices over the rationals a field? Justify your answer.

Exercise 9.21. Given the integral domain of all polynomials in x with rational coefficients, let two polynomials $P(x)$ and $Q(x)$ be in relation if $P(x) - Q(x)$ is a polynomial multiple of $x^2 + 1$.

    a. Show that this is an equivalence relation.
    b. Determine representatives for the equivalence classes.
    c. Define addition and multiplication for the equivalence classes and show that the system forms a field.
    d. Show that this field is isomorphic to the field of elements $a + bi$ with a and b rational.

QUOTIENT FIELDS

We have seen that the integers under addition and multiplication form an integral domain but not a field. However, they are embedded in the field of rational numbers, i.e., the integral domain is isomorphic to a subsystem of the field. Similarly, any integral domain may be embedded in a field called its *quotient field*. We shall now consider a process for obtaining the quotient field from an arbitrary integral domain. Comprehension of the process will be facilitated if one parallels the steps using the integral domain of integers and interpreting (a,b) as a/b.

Let F be the set of all pairs (a,b), where a and b ($b \neq 0$) are elements of an integral domain; then two elements (a,b) and (c,d) of F are equivalent if and only if $ad = bc$. The proof that this is an equivalence relation is left as an exercise. Let the equivalence class of elements equivalent to (a,b) be denoted by $\overline{a,b}$. We define addition and multiplication of equivalence classes as follows:

(1) $\overline{a, b} + \overline{c, d} = \overline{ad + bc, bd}$.

(2) $\overline{a, b} \cdot \overline{c, d} = \overline{ac, bd}$.

Note that, since the integral domain does not contain any divisors of 0, $bd \neq 0$.

▶**THEOREM 9.4.** The system $\mathscr{F}$ consisting of the set F with addition and multiplication as defined in (1) and (2) is a field.

PROOF: The proof that the system $\mathscr{F}$ is a commutative ring whose additive identity is $\overline{0, b}$ is left as an exercise. Since $\overline{1, 1} \cdot \overline{a, b} = \overline{1a, 1b} = \overline{a, b}$, F contains $\overline{1, 1}$ as the multiplicative identity. If $\overline{a, b}$ is an arbitrary nonzero element of F (i.e., $a \neq 0$), then $\overline{a, b} \cdot \overline{b, a} = \overline{ab, ab} = \overline{1, 1}$; hence, the inverse of $\overline{a, b}$ is $\overline{b, a}$.

▶**THEOREM 9.5.** Any integral domain is isomorphic to a subsystem of its quotient field.

PROOF:

1. The correspondence a to $\overline{a, 1}$ is obviously a one-to-one correspondence.

2. Since $\overline{a, 1} + \overline{b, 1} = \overline{a \cdot 1 + 1 \cdot b, 1 \cdot 1} = \overline{a + b, 1}$ and $\overline{a, 1} \cdot \overline{b, 1} = \overline{a \cdot b, 1 \cdot 1} = \overline{ab, 1}$, the sums and products in the quotient field correspond to the sums and products in the integral domain.

If the integral domain is itself a field, then it will be isomorphic to its quotient field.

Exercise 9.22. Form the quotient field for the integral domain consisting of all real numbers $a + b\sqrt{2}$ with a and b integers, and show that it is isomorphic to the field consisting of all real numbers $a + b\sqrt{2}$ with a and b rational.

Exercise 9.23. Prove that if two integral domains are isomorphic, their quotient fields are isomorphic.

Exercise 9.24. Show that a commutative ring without divisors of 0 can be embedded in a quotient field.

Exercise 9.25. Form the quotient field for the ring in Exercise 9.2h, and show that this field is isomorphic to $\mathscr{R}$.

CHAPTER X

Linear Algebras

INTRODUCTION

▶**DEFINITION 10.1.** A *linear algebra of order n over* $\mathscr{F}$ is a system consisting of a set A, operations of addition, multiplication, and scalar multiplication by elements in the field $\mathscr{F}$, and the postulates:

(1) A with addition and scalar multiplication is a vector space of dimension n over $\mathscr{F}$.
(2) Multiplication is associative on A.
(3) Multiplication is left and right distributive with respect to addition.
(4) A contains a multiplicative identity.
(5) The two multiplications are *bilinear*, that is, $(k\alpha)\beta = \alpha(k\beta) = k(\alpha\beta)$ for each α and β in A and k in F.

▶**THEOREM 10.1.** The set of all $n \times n$ matrices over a field $\mathscr{F}$ with the usual operations is a linear algebra of order n^2 over $\mathscr{F}$ (called the *total matric* algebra of degree n over $\mathscr{F}$ and denoted by $\mathscr{M}_n(\mathscr{F})$).

PROOF: That $\mathscr{M}_n(\mathscr{F})$ is a vector space of dimension n^2 over $\mathscr{F}$ was proven in Theorem 4.2. That multiplication is associative was Theorem 4.4. That multiplication is left and right distributive with respect to addition was Theorem 4.5. That I_n is the multiplicative identity was proven in Theorem 4.7. To show that the two multiplications are bilinear, we have

$$[k(a_{ij})](b_{ij}) = (ka_{ij})(b_{ij}) = \left(\sum_{h=1}^{n} ka_{ih}b_{hj} \right)$$

and

$$k[(a_{ij})(b_{ij})] = k\left(\sum_{h=1}^{n} a_{ih}b_{hj}\right) = \left(\sum_{h=1}^{n} ka_{ih}b_{hj}\right)$$

and

$$(a_{ij})[k(b_{ij})] = (a_{ij})(kb_{ij}) = \left(\sum_{h=1}^{n} a_{ih}kb_{hj}\right) = \left(\sum_{h=1}^{n} ka_{ih}b_{hj}\right)$$

Thus $(kA)B = k(AB) = A(kB)$.

▶DEFINITION 10.2. A *division algebra* is a linear algebra in which every nonzero "vector" has a multiplicative inverse.

Exercise 10.1. Show that the field $\mathscr{C}$ of complex numbers is a division algebra of order two over the field $\mathscr{R}^\sharp$ of real numbers.

Exercise 10.2 Which of the following systems are linear algebras? Division algebras?

    a. A vector space $\mathscr{V}(\mathscr{F})$ with $\alpha\beta = \epsilon_0$ for all α and β.
    b. A vector space $\mathscr{V}(\mathscr{F})$ with $\alpha\beta = \alpha$ for all α and β.
    c. All $n \times n$ diagonal matrices over $\mathscr{F}$.

Exercise 10.3. Prove that the vectors of a division algebra form a field under addition and vector multiplication if and only if the vector multiplication is commutative.

QUATERNIONS

By Exercise 10.1 the field of all complex numbers is a linear algebra of order two over the field of all real numbers. It is natural to ask whether there exist linear algebras of higher order over the real numbers which are fields. The answer is no. However, we shall show that there exists a division algebra of order four over the real numbers, usually called the algebra of *quaternions*.

We shall define multiplication for the four unit vectors ϵ_i of $\mathscr{V}_4(\mathscr{R}^\sharp)$ in Table 10.1. Since any vector in $\mathscr{V}_4(\mathscr{R}^\#)$ is a linear combination of these four vectors, the product of any two vectors in $\mathscr{V}_4(\mathscr{R}^\#)$ is defined by the use of Table 10.1.

Table 10.1

Left \ Right	ϵ_1	ϵ_2	ϵ_3	ϵ_4
ϵ_1	ϵ_1	ϵ_2	ϵ_3	ϵ_4
ϵ_2	ϵ_2	$-\epsilon_1$	ϵ_4	$-\epsilon_3$
ϵ_3	ϵ_3	$-\epsilon_4$	$-\epsilon_1$	ϵ_2
ϵ_4	ϵ_4	ϵ_3	$-\epsilon_2$	$-\epsilon_1$

For example, if $\alpha = \epsilon_1 - \epsilon_2 + 2\epsilon_3 + \epsilon_4/2$ and $\beta = -2\epsilon_1 + \epsilon_2 + 3\epsilon_3 + 2\epsilon_4$, then

$$\begin{aligned}
\alpha\beta &= -2\epsilon_1\epsilon_1 + \epsilon_1\epsilon_2 + 3\epsilon_1\epsilon_3 + 2\epsilon_1\epsilon_4 + 2\epsilon_2\epsilon_1 - \epsilon_2\epsilon_2 - 3\epsilon_2\epsilon_3 \\
&\quad - 2\epsilon_2\epsilon_4 - 4\epsilon_3\epsilon_1 + 2\epsilon_3\epsilon_2 + 6\epsilon_3\epsilon_3 + 4\epsilon_3\epsilon_4 - \epsilon_4\epsilon_1 \\
&\quad + \epsilon_4\epsilon_2/2 + 3\epsilon_4\epsilon_3/2 + \epsilon_4\epsilon_4 \\
&= -2\epsilon_1 + \epsilon_2 + 3\epsilon_3 + 2\epsilon_4 + \epsilon_1 + 2\epsilon_2 + 2\epsilon_3 - 3\epsilon_4 \\
&\quad - 6\epsilon_1 + 4\epsilon_2 - 4\epsilon_3 - 2\epsilon_4 - \epsilon_1 - 3\epsilon_2/2 + \epsilon_3/2 - \epsilon_4 \\
&= -8\epsilon_1 + 11\epsilon_2/2 + 3\epsilon_3/2 - 4\epsilon_4
\end{aligned}$$

A different notation is usually used for the quaternions. Since ϵ_1 is the multiplicative identity, we shall replace ϵ_1, ϵ_2, ϵ_3, and ϵ_4 by 1, i, j, and k, respectively. Then from the multiplication table we see that $i^2 = j^2 = k^2 = -1$, $ij = -ji = k$, $jk = -kj = i$, and $ki = -ik = j$.

▶**THEOREM 10.2.** The system $\mathscr{Q}$ of quaternions is a division algebra.

PROOF: That $\mathscr{Q}$ is a linear algebra over the real numbers is left as an exercise. For every quaternion $\alpha = a + bi + cj + dk$ there exists a *conjugate* quaternion $\alpha' = a - bi - cj - dk$. Using $|\alpha|$ to denote the real number $a^2 + b^2 + c^2 + d^2$, we have $\alpha\alpha' = (a^2 + b^2 + c^2 + d^2) + 0i + 0j + 0k = |\alpha| + 0i + 0j + 0k$. Hence for any nonzero α we have

$$\alpha^{-1} = \frac{a}{|\alpha|} - \frac{b}{|\alpha|}i - \frac{c}{|\alpha|}j - \frac{d}{|\alpha|}k$$

▶ **THEOREM 10.3.** The system of quaternions is isomorphic to a subsystem of $\mathcal{M}_4(\mathcal{R}^{\#})$.

PROOF: That the correspondence of $\alpha = a + bi + cj + dk$ to

$$\begin{pmatrix} a & b & c & d \\ -b & a & -d & c \\ -c & d & a & -b \\ -d & -c & b & a \end{pmatrix}$$

is such an isomorphism is left as an exercise.

As a generalization of Theorem 10.3, we state the following theorem without proof.

▶ **THEOREM 10.4.** Every linear algebra of order n over a field $\mathcal{F}$ is isomorphic to a subsystem of $\mathcal{M}_n(\mathcal{F})$.

Exercise 10.4. Show that the multiplication rules for i, j, and k are equivalent to $i^2 = j^2 = k^2 = ijk = -1$.

Exercise 10.5. Show that $x^2 + 1 = 0$ has infinitely many quaternions as roots.

Exercise 10.6. Show that every quaternion is a root of a quadratic equation with real coefficients.

Exercise 10.7. Show that the eight quaternions ± 1, $\pm i$, $\pm j$, $\pm k$ form a multiplicative group. State the order of each element.

Exercise 10.8. Show that $|\alpha||\beta| = |\alpha\beta|$.

Exercise 10.9. Show that the matrix in Theorem 10.3 is non-singular except when $a = b = c = d = 0$.

Exercise 10.10. Show that if, in the correspondence in Theorem 10.3, the quaternion α corresponds to the matrix A, then α^{-1} corresponds to A^{-1}.

CHAPTER XI

Boolean Algebras

INTRODUCTION

The mathematical system which arises naturally from an algebraic formulation of logic was first developed by George Boole (1815–1864). We shall discuss the system without showing its interpretation in mathematical logic.

▶**DEFINITION 11.1.** A *Boolean Algebra* $\mathscr{B}$ is a system consisting of a set B of elements, two operations $\cup$ and $\cap$,* and the following postulates:

(1a) $\cup$ is commutative on B.

(1b) $\cap$ is commutative on B.

(2a) B contains an identity element 0 with respect to $\cup$.

(2b) B contains an identity element 1 with respect to $\cap$.

(3a) $\cup$ is distributive with respect to $\cap$.

(3b) $\cap$ is distributive with respect to $\cup$.

(4) For each element b in B there is an element b' in B such that $b \cup b' = 1$ and $b \cap b' = 0$.

One very important property of Boolean Algebras which none of our previous systems has possessed is the existence of a complete symmetry in the postulates. That is, if the operations of $\cup$ and $\cap$ as well as the two identity elements 0 and 1 are interchanged in all postulates, the resulting set of postulates is identical with the original set in Definition 11.1. Since this is true of the entire set of postulates, it must also be true of any theorems deduced from them. This important concept of symmetry or "duality" is stated formally in the following principle.

---

* The symbols $\cup$ and $\cap$ are usually read "cup" and "cap," respectively.

Principle of Duality. Any theorem deducible from the postulates of a Boolean Algebra is also true when the operations $\cup$ and $\cap$ and the identity elements 0 and 1 are interchanged.

By virtue of this principle, we shall generally state pairs of dual theorems. Furthermore, it is necessary to prove only one of the pair of theorems, for the dual of its proof is the proof of the dual theorem.

►**THEOREM 11.1.** For every b in B, $b \cup b = b$.

►**THEOREM 11.1a.** For every b in B, $b \cap b = b$.

PROOF: By successive applications of postulates (2b), (4), (3b), (4), and (2a), respectively, we have

$$b = b \cap 1 = b \cap (b \cup b') = (b \cap b) \cup (b \cap b')$$
$$= (b \cap b) \cup 0 = b \cap b$$

►**THEOREM 11.2.** For every b in B, $b \cup 1 = 1$.

►**THEOREM 11.2a.** For every b in B, $b \cap 0 = 0$.

PROOF: By successive applications of postulates (2a), (4), (3b), (2a), and (4), respectively, we have

$$b \cap 0 = 0 \cup (b \cap 0) = (b \cap b') \cup (b \cap 0)$$
$$= b \cap (b' \cup 0) = b \cap b' = 0$$

►**THEOREM 11.3.** If $0 = 1$, then $b = 1$ for every b in B, that is, B contains only one element.

PROOF: By successive applications of postulate (2a), the hypothesis, and Theorem 11.2, respectively, we have

$$b = b \cup 0 = b \cup 1 = 1$$

►**THEOREM 11.4.** For every a and b in B, $a \cup (a \cap b) = a$.

▶**THEOREM 11.4a.** For every a and b in B, $a \cap (a \cup b) = a$.

PROOF: By successive applications of postulates (1a), (1b), (2a), (3a), Theorem 11.2a, and postulate (2a), respectively, we have

$$a \cap (a \cup b) = a \cap (b \cup a) = (b \cup a) \cap a$$
$$= (b \cup a) \cap (0 \cup a) = (b \cap 0) \cup a = 0 \cup a = a$$

▶**THEOREM 11.5.** $\cup$ is associative on B.

▶**THEOREM 11.5a.** $\cap$ is associative on B.

PROOF: We wish to show that $a \cap (b \cap c) = (a \cap b) \cap c$ for any a, b, and c in B. Let $L = a \cap (b \cap c)$ and $R = (a \cap b) \cap c$. Then $a \cup L = a \cup [a \cap (b \cap c)] = (a \cup a) \cap [a \cup (b \cap c)] = a \cap [a \cup (b \cap c)] = a$ by postulate (3a) and Theorem 11.4. Similarly, $a \cup R = a \cup [(a \cap b) \cap c] = [a \cup (a \cap b)] \cap (a \cup c) = a \cap (a \cup c) = a$. Thus $a \cup L = a \cup R$. Furthermore, $a' \cup L = a' \cup [a \cap (b \cap c)] = (a' \cup a) \cap [a' \cup (b \cap c)] = 1 \cap [a' \cup (b \cap c)] = a' \cup (b \cap c)$ and $a' \cup R = a' \cup [(a \cap b) \cap c] = [a' \cup (a \cap b)] \cap (a' \cup c) = [(a' \cup a) \cap (a' \cup b)] \cap (a' \cup c) = [1 \cap (a' \cup b)] \cap (a' \cup c) = (a' \cup b) \cap (a' \cup c) = a' \cup (b \cap c)$. Thus $a' \cup L = a' \cup R$. Then $(a \cup L) \cap (a' \cup L) = (a \cup R) \cap (a' \cup R)$, $(a \cap a') \cup L = (a \cap a') \cup R$, $0 \cup L = 0 \cup R$, and $L = R$.

The justification of each step in the proof is left as an exercise.

▶**THEOREM 11.6.** The element b' corresponding to each b in B is unique.

PROOF: Assume that there are two such elements, b' and b'', satisfying postulate (4). Then $b' = 1 \cap b' = (b \cup b'') \cap b' = (b \cap b') \cup (b'' \cap b') = 0 \cup (b'' \cap b') = b'' \cap b' = b' \cap b'' = 0 \cup (b' \cap b'') = (b \cap b'') \cup (b' \cap b'') = (b \cup b') \cap b'' = 1 \cap b'' = b''$.

▶**THEOREM II.7.** For every b in B, $(b')' = b$.

PROOF: $(b')' = 1 \cap (b')' = (b \cup b') \cap (b')' = [b \cap (b')'] \cup [b' \cap (b')'] = [b \cap (b')'] \cup 0 = 0 \cup [b \cap (b')'] = (b \cap b') \cup [b \cap (b')'] = b \cap [b' \cup (b')'] = b \cap 1 = b.$

▶**THEOREM II.8.** For every a and b in B, $(a \cup b)' = a' \cap b'$.

▶**THEOREM II.8a.** For every a and b in B, $(a \cap b)' = a' \cup b'$.

PROOF: $(a \cap b) \cap (a' \cup b') = [(a \cap b) \cap a'] \cup [(a \cap b) \cap b'] = (0 \cap b) \cup (a \cap 0) = 0 \cup 0 = 0$, whereas $(a \cap b) \cup (a' \cup b') = [a \cup (a' \cup b')] \cap [b \cup (a' \cup b')] = (1 \cup b') \cap (1 \cup a') = 1 \cap 1 = 1$. Then by Theorem 11.6 $(a \cap b)' = a' \cup b'$.

Exercise 11.1. Show that the set of three elements a, b, c with operations $\cup$ and $\cap$ as defined by the following tables is not a Boolean Algebra.

$\cup$	a	b	c
a	a	a	c
b	a	b	c
c	c	c	c

$\cap$	a	b	c
a	a	b	a
b	b	b	b
c	a	b	c

Which element is 0? 1? a'? b'? c'?

Exercise 11.2. Prove that if in a Boolean Algebra $\mathscr{B}$ $a \cap b = a \cap c$ and $a \cup b = a \cup c$ for any a, b, and c in B, then $b = c$.

Exercise 11.3. Prove that for any a, b, and c in a Boolean Algebra $(a \cap b) \cup (b \cap c) \cup (c \cap a) = (a \cup b) \cap (b \cup c) \cap (c \cup a)$. What is the dual of this statement?

Exercise 11.4. Show that in any Boolean Algebra $0' = 1$ and $1' = 0$.

Exercise 11.5. Let B be a subset of the positive integers and for any a and b in B let $a \cup b$ be the least common multiple of a and b and let $a \cap b$ be the highest common factor of a and b.

    a. Show that $\mathscr{B}$ is a Boolean Algebra when B is the set of integers 1, 2, 5, 7, 10, 14, 35, and 70.

    b. Show that the set 1, 2, 3, 6, 9, and 18 is not a Boolean Algebra under these operations.

Exercise 11.6. Show that there exists a Boolean Algebra with only two elements. Give the tables for the two operations.

Exercise 11.7. Show that the set of four elements a, b, c, and d with the operations $\cup$ and $\cap$ as defined by the following tables is a Boolean Algebra.

$\cup$	a	b	c	d
a	a	b	c	d
b	b	b	d	d
c	c	d	c	d
d	d	d	d	d

$\cap$	a	b	c	d
a	a	a	a	a
b	a	b	a	b
c	a	a	c	c
d	a	b	c	d

THE BOOLEAN ALGEBRA OF SETS

One of the most important examples of a Boolean Algebra is based on the set of all subsets of a given set. Let I be a set of elements and let B be the set of all subsets of I, including I and the void set V (the set containing no elements). For any two sets C and D in B, let $C \cup D$ be the set consisting of all elements in C or D (or both) and let $C \cap D$ be the set of all elements in both C and D.

That $\cup$ and $\cap$ are both commutative operations on B follows directly from their definitions. Furthermore, for any C in B, $C \cup V = C$ and $C \cap I = C$; hence V and I are the identity elements 0 and 1, respectively.

To show that postulate (3a) is satisfied, it is necessary to show that $C \cup (D \cap E) = (C \cup D) \cap (C \cup E)$ for any C, D, and E in B. In order to be in the set $C \cup (D \cap E)$, an element must be in C or in $D \cap E$, that is, it must be in C or in both D and E. Then the element must be in both $C \cup D$ and $C \cup E$. Hence it is in $(C \cup D) \cap (C \cup E)$. Thus every element in $C \cup (D \cap E)$ is also in $(C \cup D) \cap (C \cup E)$ and the former is a subset of the latter. Also an element of $(C \cup D) \cap (C \cup E)$ must be in both $C \cup D$ and $C \cup E$. Thus it must be in either C or D and at the same time in either C or E, whence the element must be in C or in both D and E. But this says that the element is in C or in $D \cap E$, that is, it is in $C \cup (D \cap E)$. Thus $(C \cup D) \cap (C \cup E)$ is also a subset of $C \cup (D \cap E)$ and the two are equal. Postulate (3b) is verified similarly.

For each set C in B, let C' be the set of all those elements which are in I but not in C. Then obviously $C \cup C' = I$ and $C \cap C' = V$ so that C' is the element satisfying postulate (4).

Thus the system $\mathscr{B}$ consisting of the set B and the operations $\cup$ and $\cap$ defined above is a Boolean Algebra. Many of the well-known properties of sets are stated in Theorems 11.1 through 11.8a.

Exercise 11.8. Show that the Boolean Algebra of all subsets of a set of two elements is isomorphic to the Boolean Algebra in Exercise 11.7.

BOOLEAN ALGEBRA OF SWITCHING NETWORKS

Let us consider another important example of a Boolean Algebra: electrical networks containing switches. (Only the most fundamental knowledge of electricity is required to follow the discussion.)

Each switch can be either open or closed. A closed switch permits the flow of current whereas an open switch does not. Let us denote switches by letters p, q, r, etc., and assign the values 1 and 0 to denote closed and open switches, respectively.

We shall also use 1 and 0 to denote networks through which current does and does not flow, respectively.

The simplest switching network is a single wire containing a single switch p:

├——— p ———┤

The value of this network is identical with the value of p. Two switches, p and q, can be connected in series:

├——— p ——— q ———┤

Current will flow through this network if and only if both p and q are closed. The values of the network corresponding to the possible values of p and q are given in Table 11.1. But this is

TABLE 11.1

p	q	$p \cap q$ (network)
0	1	0
0	0	0
1	0	0
1	1	1

exactly the table for the elements 0 and 1 under the operation $\cap$ in a Boolean Algebra (see Exercise 11.6). Thus we shall denote the fact that switches p and q are connected in series by $p \cap q$.

Two switches can also be connected in parallel:

Current will flow through this network if at least one switch is closed. The values of the network for the possible values of p and q are given in Table 11.2. But again this table represents the

TABLE 11.2

p	q	$p \cup q$ (network)
0	0	0
0	1	1
1	0	1
1	1	1

elements 0 and 1 under the operation $\cup$ in a Boolean Algebra. Thus we shall denote two switches, p and q, connected in parallel by $p \cup q$.*

Networks involving combinations of series and parallel connections are expressed accordingly. For instance, the series of two pairs of parallel switches

would be denoted by $(p \cup q) \cap (r \cup s)$.

But switches need not act independently of each other. Two or more switches can be coupled so that they open and close simultaneously. Such switches will be denoted by the same letter. Furthermore, two switches may be coupled so that when one opens the other closes. For such switches we denote those in one position by a letter and those in the other position by the same letter with a prime, for example, p and p'.

---

* Although it is customary to represent the operation $\cup$ and $\cap$ in the Boolean Algebra of circuits by $+$ and juxtaposition, respectively, the former are employed for uniformity of notation.

Thus for any switching network we have a corresponding algebraic expression in which each letter can be assigned a value of 0 or 1 and the expression itself has a value of 0 or 1. We shall show that the system consisting of these algebraic expressions for switching networks is a Boolean Algebra.

That $\cup$ and $\cap$ are commutative operations follows directly from their definitions and Tables 11.1 and 11.2. With 0 and 1 denoting switches that are open and closed, respectively, postulates (2a) and (2b) are satisfied.

The network represented by $p \cup (q \cap r)$ will permit current to flow if either p is closed and/or both q and r are closed. But this means that p and/or q as well as p and/or r are closed. But in this form the network is represented by $(p \cup q) \cap (p \cup r)$. Thus $p \cup (q \cap r) = (p \cup q) \cap (p \cup r)$ and postulate (3a) is satisfied. Postulate (3b) is verified similarly.

That $p \cup p' = 1$ and $p \cap p' = 0$ is a direct consequence of the definition of p'. Thus all of the postulates of Definition 11.1 are satisfied and this system is a Boolean Algebra.

Making use of this fact, a given network can be expressed algebraically, that expression modified by means of the postulates and theorems of Boolean Algebra, and the network corresponding to the new expression will perform the function of the original network. Many switching networks may be simplified by this procedure.

For example, the algebraic expression for the network

$$\text{(1)}$$

is $(a \cap b) \cup (a \cap b \cap c) \cup (a' \cap c)$. Since $d \cup (d \cap c) = d$, if we let $d = a \cap b$, we have $(a \cap b) \cup (a \cap b \cap c) \cup (a' \cap c) = (a \cap b) \cup (a' \cap c)$. Hence the corresponding network

$$\text{(2)}$$

will function the same as network (1) and involves three fewer switches.

Exercise 11.9. Given the network

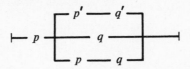

a. Write the algebraic expression for this network.
b. Simplify this expression as much as possible.
c. Give the diagram of the network corresponding to this simpler expression.

ORDER IN A BOOLEAN ALGEBRA

In any Boolean Algebra we can define an order relation which possesses some of the familiar properties of the "less than or equal to" relation on $\mathscr{R}^{\#}$ but which also has some different properties.

▶**DEFINITION 11.2.** For any two elements a and b of a Boolean Algebra, $a \leq b$ if and only if $a \cup b = b$.*

▶**THEOREM 11.9.** For every element b of a Boolean Algebra, $b \leq b$.

PROOF: This theorem follows directly from Theorem 11.1.

▶**THEOREM 11.10.** For every a and b in a Boolean Algebra, if $a \leq b$ and $b \leq a$, then $a = b$.

PROOF: Exercise.

▶**THEOREM 11.11.** For every a, b, and c in a Boolean Algebra, if $a \leq b$ and $b \leq c$, then $a \leq c$.

---

* The symbol "$\leq$" is read "under."

PROOF: By Definition 11.2 $a \leq b$ and $b \leq c$ mean that $a \cup b = b$ and $b \cup c = c$. Then $a \cup c = a \cup (b \cup c) = (a \cup b) \cup c = b \cup c = c$. Hence $a \leq c$.

Theorems 11.9, 11.10, and 11.11 state properties of the $\leq$ relation on a Boolean Algebra which are analogous to those of the $\leq$ relation on $\mathscr{R}^{\#}$. However, the $\leq$ relation on $\mathscr{B}$ is in other respects much different from the $\leq$ relation on $\mathscr{R}^{\#}$. For example, for any two different elements a and b in $\mathscr{R}^{\#}$, either $a \leq b$ or $b \leq a$. This is not true in a Boolean Algebra with more than two elements. If b is any element in B such that $b \neq 0$ and $b \neq 1$, then $b' \neq 0$ and $b' \neq 1$. Since $b \cup b' = 1$, $b' \cup b \neq b$ and $b \cup b' \neq b'$. Thus $b' \not\leq b$ and $b \not\leq b'$.

▶**THEOREM 11.12.** For every b in a Boolean Algebra, $0 \leq b \leq 1$.

PROOF: Exercise.

From Theorem 11.12 it follows that 0 and 1 are lower and upper bounds, respectively, for all elements in a Boolean Algebra.

▶**THEOREM 11.13.** For every a and b in a Boolean Algebra, $a \cup b$ is the least upper bound of a and b, whereas $a \cap b$ is their greatest lower bound.

PROOF: Since $a \cup (a \cup b) = a \cup b$ and $b \cup (a \cup b) = a \cup b$, we have $a \leq (a \cup b)$ and $b \leq (a \cup b)$. Thus $a \cup b$ is an upper bound for a and b. To show that it is a least upper bound, let c be any upper bound of a and b; then $a \leq c$ and $b \leq c$, whence $a \cup c = c$ and $b \cup c = c$. Then $(a \cup b) \cup c = a \cup (b \cup c) = a \cup c = c$ so that $(a \cup b) \leq c$. Thus $a \cup b$ is the least upper bound of a and b. The proof that $a \cap b$ is the greatest lower bound of a and b is left as an exercise.

Exercise 11.10. Show that for any a, b, and c in a Boolean Algebra, if $a \leq b$, then $(a \cup c) \leq (b \cup c)$ and $(a \cap c) \leq (b \cap c)$.

Exercise 11.11. Show that, for any a and b in a Boolean Algebra, $a \leq b$ if and only if $a \cap b = a$.

Exercise 11.12. Show that, for any a and b in a Boolean Algebra, $a \leq b$ if and only if $a \cap b' = 0$.

Exercise 11.13. Show that, for any a and b in a Boolean Algebra, $a \leq b$ if and only if $b' \leq a'$.

Exercise 11.14. Show that, in a Boolean Algebra of sets, "$A \leq B$" is equivalent to "A is a subset of B."

BOOLEAN RINGS

In any Boolean Algebra $\mathscr{B}$ it is possible to define a ring. In order to do this, we define two new operations $\oplus$ and $\cdot$ in terms of the operations $\cup$ and $\cap$ of the Boolean Algebra. For any a and b in B we define

(1) $a \oplus b = (a \cap b') \cup (a' \cap b)$

(2) $a \cdot b \ = a \cap b$

►**THEOREM 11.14.** The system consisting of the set B of a Boolean Algebra $\mathscr{B}$ with the operations $\oplus$ and $\cdot$ defined in (1) and (2) is a commutative ring with unity, called a *Boolean Ring*.

PROOF: That $\oplus$ and $\cdot$ are operations on B follows from their definitions and the fact that $\cup$ and $\cap$ are operations on B. We first show that B with the operation $\oplus$ is an Abelian group. That $\oplus$ is associative on B is left as an exercise. That $\oplus$ is commutative on B is shown by $a \oplus b = (a \cap b') \cup (a' \cap b) = (b' \cap a) \cup (b \cap a') = (b \cap a') \cup (b' \cap a) = b \oplus a$. Since $a \oplus 0 = (a \cap 0') \cup (a' \cap 0) = (a \cap 1) \cup (a' \cap 0) = a \cup 0 = a$, the identity element for $\oplus$ is 0. Furthermore, $a \oplus a = (a \cap a') \cup (a \cap a') = 0 \cup 0 = 0$ so that each element is its own additive inverse. That operation $\cdot$ is associative follows from its definition and Theorem 11.5a. Also $\cdot$ is commutative on B since $\cap$ is commutative on B. Then $a \cdot (b \oplus c) = a \cap [(b \cap c') \cup (b' \cap c)] = (a \cap b \cap c') \cup (a \cap b' \cap c)$, whereas $(a \cdot b) \oplus (a \cdot$

$c) = [(a \cap b) \cap (a \cap c)'] \cup [(a \cap b)' \cap (a \cap c)] = [(a \cap b) \cap (a' \cup c')] \cup [(a' \cup b') \cap (a \cap c)] = (a \cap b \cap a') \cup (a \cap b \cap c') \cup (a \cap c \cap a') \cup (a \cap c \cap b') = (0 \cap b) \cup (a \cap b \cap c') \cup (0 \cap c) \cup (a \cap b' \cap c) = 0 \cup (a \cap b \cap c') \cup 0 \cup (a \cap b' \cap c) = (a \cap b \cap c') \cup (a \cap b' \cap c).$ Thus $a \cdot (b \oplus c) = (a \cdot b) \oplus (a \cdot c)$ and $\cdot$ is distributive with respect to $\oplus$. Finally, $a \cdot 1 = a \cap 1 = a$ shows that 1 is the multiplicative identity.

▶ **THEOREM 11.15.** For any a and b in a Boolean Ring, $a \oplus b = 0$ if and only if $a = b$.

PROOF: Exercise.

▶ **THEOREM 11.16.** For any a in a Boolean Ring, $a \cdot a = a$.

PROOF: Exercise.

▶ **THEOREM 11.17.** A Boolean Ring with more than two elements contains "divisors of 0."

PROOF: By hypothesis the Boolean Ring contains two different elements a and b such that $a \neq 0$ and $b \neq 0$. Then $a \oplus b$ is in the Boolean Ring and $a \oplus b \neq 0$ by Theorem 11.15. But $a \cdot b$ is in the ring also and $(a \cdot b) \cdot (a \oplus b) = (a \cdot b \cdot a) \oplus (a \cdot b \cdot b) = (a \cdot b) \oplus (a \cdot b) = 0$. Thus if $a \cdot b \neq 0$, $a \cdot b$ and $a \oplus b$ are divisors of 0. On the other hand, if $a \cdot b = 0$, then a and b are divisors of 0.

Exercise 11.15. Show that for any a, b, and c in a Boolean Ring, if $a \oplus b = c$, then $a = c \oplus b$.

Exercise 11.16. Show that the definition of the operation $\oplus$ given in (1) on page 123 is equivalent to $a \oplus b = (a \cup b) \cap (a' \cup b')$.

Exercise 11.17. Is the Boolean Ring formed from the four-element Boolean Algebra of Exercise 11.7 isomorphic to the ring $\mathscr{J}_4$?

CHAPTER XII

Square Matrices

DETERMINANTS

We shall first consider a function of a square matrix A, called the determinant of A and denoted by det(A). In order to give a relatively simple definition of det(A), we first need some preliminary facts concerning permutations.

Given a set of n elements, any particular sequence containing each element once and only once is a *permutation* of these n elements taken n at a time. It is easy to show that there are exactly $n!$ permutations of n things taken n at a time.

Any one particular permutation is chosen to define the natural order of the elements. Two elements of a permutation are said to form a *permanence* if they appear in their natural order regardless of intervening elements; otherwise they form an *inversion*. For example, taking 1, 2, 3, 4, 5, with numerical order as their natural order, the permutation 3, 1, 4, 2, 5 has seven permanences and three inversions. A permutation is called $\begin{Bmatrix} \text{odd} \\ \text{even} \end{Bmatrix}$ if it has an $\begin{Bmatrix} \text{odd} \\ \text{even} \end{Bmatrix}$ number of inversions.

▶THEOREM 12.1. Interchanging two elements of a permutation changes the number of inversions by an odd number.

PROOF: Interchanging two adjacent elements of a permutation changes the number of the inversions by one. To interchange two nonadjacent elements a and b of a permutation, assume there are k intervening elements. The segment of the permutation we are concerned with appears as $a\mathrm{K}b$, where K is a sequence of k elements. To produce $ba\mathrm{K}$ requires $k + 1$ interchanges of adjacent elements. Then to produce $b\mathrm{K}a$ requires k additional interchanges of adjacent elements. Thus the interchange of any two elements changes the number of inversions by an odd number.

▶**THEOREM 12.2.** Of all the $n!$ permutations of n elements $(n > 1)$, exactly half are even.

PROOF: Suppose there are k odd permutations and h even permutations. Interchanging the same two elements in each odd permutation produces a set of distinct even permutations. Hence $k \le h$. Similarly, by interchanging elements in the members of the set of all even permutations we obtain $h \le k$.

▶**THEOREM 12.3.** To restore an $\begin{Bmatrix} \text{odd} \\ \text{even} \end{Bmatrix}$ permutation to its natural order requires an $\begin{Bmatrix} \text{odd} \\ \text{even} \end{Bmatrix}$ number of interchanges of elements.

PROOF: Exercise.

Let us now return to the definition of det(A) as proposed at the beginning of this chapter. We shall take numerical order as natural order for permutations of integers.

▶**DEFINITION 12.1.** The *determinant* of an $n \times n$ matrix A is given by

$$\det(A) = \sum \text{sgn}\,(c_1, c_2, \ldots, c_n) a_{1c_1} a_{2c_2} \ldots a_{nc_n}$$

where the sum is over all permutations $c_1, \ldots, c_n$ of the integers $1, \ldots, n$ and sgn $(c_1, \ldots, c_n)$ is $\begin{Bmatrix} -1 \\ +1 \end{Bmatrix}$ if the permutation $c_1, \ldots, c_n$ is $\begin{Bmatrix} \text{odd} \\ \text{even} \end{Bmatrix}$.

Thus det(A) is a sum of $n!$ terms, each having a well-defined sign. Any term is a product of n elements, one and only one from each row and column of A. From this the following theorem is obvious.

▶THEOREM 12.4. If any row or column of A consists entirely of 0's, then $\det(A) = 0$.

▶THEOREM 12.5. Let B be the matrix formed by interchanging any two rows of A. Then $\det(B) = -\det(A)$.

PROOF: Suppose that B is formed from A by interchanging the ith and jth rows $(i < j)$. Then $b_{ik} = a_{jk}$ and $b_{jk} = a_{ik}$ for $k = 1, 2, \ldots, n$, whereas $b_{hk} = a_{hk}$ for all $h \neq i, j$. A typical term of $\det(B)$ is

$$\text{sgn}\ (c_1, \ldots, c_i, \ldots, c_j, \ldots, c_n) b_{1c_1} \ldots b_{ic_i} \ldots b_{jc_j} \ldots b_{nc_n}$$
$$= \text{sgn}\ (c_1, \ldots, c_i, \ldots, c_j, \ldots, c_n) a_{1c_1} \ldots a_{jc_i} \ldots a_{ic_j} \ldots a_{nc_n}$$
$$= -\text{sgn}\ (c_1, \ldots, c_j, \ldots, c_i, \ldots, c_n) a_{1c_1} \ldots a_{ic_j} \ldots a_{jc_i} \ldots a_{nc_n}$$

by Theorem 12.1. But this is the negative of a typical term of $\det(A)$. Thus each term of $\det(B)$ is the negative of the corresponding term of $\det(A)$.

▶COROLLARY. If two rows of A are identical, then $\det(A) = 0$.

▶THEOREM 12.6. Let B be the matrix formed by multiplying one row of A by k. Then $\det(B) = k \det(A)$.

PROOF: Exercise.

▶COROLLARY. $\det(kA) = k^n \det(A)$.

▶THEOREM 12.7. Let B be the matrix formed by adding a multiple of one row of A to a different row. Then $\det(B) = \det(A)$.

PROOF: Without loss of generality, we shall add k times the second row to the first row. Then $\det(B) = \Sigma\ \text{sgn}\ (c_1, \ldots, c_n) \times (a_{1c_1} + ka_{2c_1})a_{2c_2} \ldots a_{nc_n} = \Sigma\ \text{sgn}\ (c_1, \ldots, c_n)a_{1c_1}a_{2c_2} \ldots a_{nc_n} + k\Sigma\ \text{sgn}\ (c_1, \ldots, c_n)a_{2c_1}a_{2c_2} \ldots a_{nc_n} = \det(A) + k \det(C)$, where C is the matrix obtained from A by replacing the first row by the second row. By the corollary to Theorem 12.5, $\det(C) = 0$.

▶**THEOREM 12.8.** If A is singular, $\det(A) = 0$.

PROOF: Exercise.

Although we are concerned only with square matrices, we make the following general definition (as in Exercise 4.17).

▶**DEFINITION 12.2.** The *transpose* of a matrix ${}_mA_n$, denoted by ${}_mA_n{}^T$, is a matrix ${}_nB_m$ such that $b_{ij} = a_{ji}$ for all i and j.

▶**THEOREM 12.9.** $\det(A^T) = \det(A)$.

PROOF: It is obvious that the terms of $\det(A^T)$ and $\det(A)$ are identical except possibly for sign. A typical term of $\det(A)$ is $\operatorname{sgn}(c_1, \ldots, c_n)a_{1c_1} \ldots a_{nc_n}$. Putting the second index into numerical order gives $\operatorname{sgn}(c_1, \ldots, c_n)a_{r_11} \ldots a_{r_nn}$. But every removal of an inversion in the second subscript produces an inversion in the first. Thus $\operatorname{sgn}(r_1, \ldots, r_n) = \operatorname{sgn}(c_1, \ldots, c_n)$ and $\det(A) = \Sigma \operatorname{sgn}(c_1, \ldots, c_n)a_{1c_1} \ldots a_{nc_n} = \Sigma \operatorname{sgn}(r_1, \ldots, r_n) a_{r_11} \ldots a_{r_nn} = \det(A^T)$.

By virtue of Theorem 12.9 all theorems on determinants are also valid with the word "row" replaced by the word "column."

Every term of $\det(A)$ contains one element of the ith row of A. In particular, the element a_{ij} appears in $(n-1)!$ terms. Collecting the terms containing $a_{ij} (j = 1, \ldots, n)$, we have

$$\det(A) = a_{i1}A_{i1} + a_{i2}A_{i2} + \ldots + a_{in}A_{in} = \sum_{j=1}^{n} a_{ij}A_{ij}.$$ The expression A_{ij} is called the *cofactor* of a_{ij}. It consists of $(n-1)!$ terms, none of which contains elements of the ith row or jth column. Let M_{ij} be the $(n-1) \times (n-1)$ "submatrix" or *minor* of A obtained by deleting the ith row and the jth column of A.

▶**THEOREM 12.10.** $A_{ij} = (-1)^{i+j} \det(M_{ij})$.

PROOF: The permutation $c_i, c_1, \ldots, c_{i-1}, c_{i+1}, \ldots, c_n$ is obtained from $c_1, \ldots, c_{i-1}, c_i, c_{i+1}, \ldots, c_n$ by $i-1$ interchanges of adjacent elements. Hence by Theorem 12.1 sgn $(c_i, c_1, \ldots, c_{i-1}, c_{i+1}, \ldots, c_n) = (-1)^{i-1}$ sgn $(c_1, \ldots, c_{i-1}, c_i, c_{i+1}, \ldots, c_n)$. Also

$$\operatorname{sgn}(c_i, c_1, \ldots, c_{i-1}, c_{i+1}, \ldots, c_n) = (-1)^{c_i-1}$$
$$\times \operatorname{sgn}(c_1, \ldots, c_{i-1}, c_{i+1} \ldots, c_n)$$

since c_i is followed by $c_i - 1$ smaller c_j's. Thus

$$\operatorname{sgn}(c_1, \ldots, c_{i-1}, j, c_{i+1}, \ldots, c_n) = (-1)^{i+j}$$
$$\times \operatorname{sgn}(c_1, \ldots, c_{i-1}, c_{i+1}, \ldots, c_n).$$

But a typical term of A_{ij} is

$$\operatorname{sgn}(c_1, \ldots, c_{i-1}, j, c_{i+1}, \ldots, c_n) a_{1c_1} \ldots a_{(i-1)c_{i-1}} a_{(i+1)c_{i+1}} \ldots a_{nc_n}$$
$$= (-1)^{i+j} \operatorname{sgn}(c_1, \ldots, c_{i-1}, c_{i+1}, \ldots, c_n) a_{1c_1} \ldots a_{(i-1)c_{i-1}}$$
$$\times a_{(i+1)c_{i+1}} \ldots a_{nc_n},$$

which is $(-1)^{i+j}$ times the corresponding typical term of $\det(M_{ij})$.

We have now proved:

▶**THEOREM 12.11.** $\det(A) = \sum_{j=1}^{n} (-1)^{i+j} a_{ij} \det(M_{ij})$ for any i, and $\det(A) = \sum_{i=1}^{n} (-1)^{i+j} a_{ij} \det(M_{ij})$ for any j.

By means of Theorem 12.11 we are able to express the determinant of an $n \times n$ matrix in terms of n determinants of $(n-1) \times (n-1)$ matrices. This process is commonly called *expansion by minors*.

▶**THEOREM 12.12.** For $i \neq k$, $\sum_{j=1}^{n} a_{ij} A_{kj} = 0$.

PROOF: Using Theorem 12.7, we have $\det(A) = \sum_{j=1}^{n} a_{kj} A_{kj} = \sum_{j=1}^{n} (a_{kj} + a_{ij}) A_{kj} = \sum_{j=1}^{n} a_{kj} A_{kj} + \sum_{j=1}^{n} a_{ij} A_{kj} = \det(A) + \sum_{j=1}^{n} a_{ij} A_{kj}.$

▶**DEFINITION 12.3.** The matrix adj(A), called the *adjoint of* A, is the transpose of the matrix whose elements are the cofactors A_{ij} of the corresponding elements a_{ij} of A. That is, adj(A) = $(A_{ij})^{\mathrm{T}}$.

▶**THEOREM 12.13.** adj(A) A = A adj(A) = det(A) I.

PROOF: Exercise. (*Hint*: Theorem 12.12.)

▶**COROLLARY.** $A^{-1} = \dfrac{1}{\det(A)}$ adj(A).

Exercise 12.1. Compute the determinants of the coefficient matrices in Exercise 5.1 through Exercise 5.4.

Exercise 12.2. Prove that if in A, $a_{ij} = 0$ for $i < j$, then det(A) = $\prod\limits_{i=1}^{n} a_{ii}$.

Exercise 12.3. Show that the determinant of the 4 × 4 Vandermonde matrix

$$\begin{vmatrix} 1 & a & a^2 & a^3 \\ 1 & b & b^2 & b^3 \\ 1 & c & c^2 & c^3 \\ 1 & d & d^2 & d^3 \end{vmatrix}$$

is $(b - a)(c - a)(d - a)(c - b)(d - b)(d - c)$.

Exercise 12.4. Generalize Exercise 12.3 to an $n \times n$ Vandermonde matrix.

Exercise 12.5. Prove that if $_nA_n{}^{\mathrm{T}} = -_nA_n$, that is, $a_{ij} = -a_{ji}$ for all i and j, and n is odd, then det(A) = 0.

Exercise 12.6. Show that the determinant of a diagonal matrix is the product of the diagonal elements, and hence that $\det(I_n) = 1$.

Exercise 12.7. det(A) = 0 if and only if A is singular.

Exercise 12.8. Given the following matrix A, find det(A), adj(A), and (by the corollary to Theorem 12.13) A^{-1}.

$$A = \begin{pmatrix} 1 & 2 & 3 \\ 0 & 2 & 1 \\ -1 & 1 & -2 \end{pmatrix}$$

CHARACTERISTIC POLYNOMIALS

We have seen that an $n \times n$ matrix A over $\mathscr{F}$ represents a linear transformation of an n dimensional vector space over $\mathscr{F}$. Under such a transformation the zero vector is transformed into itself. It is natural to ask whether there exist other vectors which transform into themsleves or, more generally, into scalar multiples of themselves. In other words, does there exist a vector ξ (a $1 \times n$ matrix) and a scalar y such that $A\xi^T = y\xi^T$? This equation can be written as $y\xi^T - A\xi^T = (yI_n = A)\xi^T = {}_nZ_1$. Obviously $\xi = \epsilon_0$ and y arbitrary is a solution of this matrix equation. In order for this equation to have solutions with $\xi \neq \epsilon_0$, the matrix $yI_n - A$ must be singular by the corollary to Theorem 4.11. Then by Theorem 12.8 $\det(yI_n - A) = 0$. Since

$$yI_n - A = \begin{pmatrix} y - a_{11} & -a_{12} & -a_{13} & \cdots & -a_{1n} \\ -a_{21} & y - a_{22} & -a_{23} & \cdots & -a_{2n} \\ -a_{31} & -a_{32} & y - a_{33} & \cdots & -a_{3n} \\ \cdot & & & & \cdot \\ \cdot & & & & \cdot \\ \cdot & & & & \cdot \\ -a_{n1} & -a_{n2} & -a_{n3} & \cdots & y - a_{nn} \end{pmatrix}$$

it follows from Definition 12.1 that $\det(yI_n - A)$ is a polynomial of degree n in y over $\mathscr{F}$.

▶DEFINITION 12.4. The nth degree polynomial $\det(yI_n - A) = C_A(n,y)$ is called the *characteristic polynomial* of A, and $C_A(n,y) = 0$ is called the *characteristic equation*.

▶THEOREM 12.14. If $C_A(n,y) = \sum_{i=0}^{n} b_i y^i$, then $b_n = 1$ and $b_0 = (-1)^n \det(A)$.

PROOF: Exercise.

Exercise 12.9. Find $C_A(y)$ for

$$A = \begin{pmatrix} 1 & 0 & 0 & 0 \\ 0 & 0 & 0 & 1 \\ 0 & 0 & 1 & 0 \\ 0 & 1 & 0 & 0 \end{pmatrix}$$

Exercise 12.10. Find $C_A(y)$ for

$$A = \begin{pmatrix} 2 & 1 \\ 2 & 0 \end{pmatrix}$$

CHARACTERISTIC VALUES

For every root y_i in $\mathscr{F}$ of $C_A(y) = 0$, the matrix $y_i I_n - A$ is singular and hence of rank less than n. Thus by Theorem 5.3 the system $(y_i I_n - A)\xi^{\mathrm{T}} = {}_n Z_1$ in n unknowns has nonzero solutions. Thus *for any square matrix there exist vectors which are transformed into multiples of themselves provided the characteristic equation has at least one root in $\mathscr{F}$.*

Although the extension of the ensuing discussion to many other fields is readily accomplished, we shall henceforth confine ourselves to matrices over the field $\mathscr{C}$ of complex numbers.

▶**DEFINITION 12.5.** The roots $y_1, \ldots, y_n$ of $C_A(n,y) = 0$ are called the *characteristic values* of A. (These are also frequently referred to as *eigenvalues* or *proper values* of A.)

Thus for matrices over $\mathscr{C}$, we have the following theorem.

▶**THEOREM 12.15.** For a matrix ${}_n A_n$ over $\mathscr{C}$, corresponding to each distinct *characteristic value* y_i, there exists at least one nonzero vector ξ_i in $\mathscr{V}_n(\mathscr{C})$ satisfying $(y_i I_n - A)\xi_i^{\mathrm{T}} = {}_n Z_1$.

The vectors ξ_i determined by Theorem 12.15 are called *characteristic vectors*. If a matrix A is over a subfield $\mathscr{F}$ of $\mathscr{C}$ and a particular characteristic value y_i is also in $\mathscr{F}$, then the corresponding ξ_i is in $\mathscr{V}_n(\mathscr{F})$.

Exercise 12.11. Prove that any 2×2 matrix over the field of real numbers with $a_{ij} = a_{ji}$ has real characteristic values.

Exercise 12.12. Compute the characteristic values and the characteristic vectors of the following matrices over $\mathscr{C}$.

a. $\begin{pmatrix} 4 & 2 \\ 2 & 1 \end{pmatrix}$

b. $\begin{pmatrix} 2 & 1 \\ 4 & -1 \end{pmatrix}$

c. $\begin{pmatrix} 6 & 2 \\ -2 & 1 \end{pmatrix}$

d. $\begin{pmatrix} 3 + 2i & 1 + i \\ 1 - i & 3 - 2i \end{pmatrix}$

e. $\begin{pmatrix} \cos \theta & \sin \theta \\ -\sin \theta & \cos \theta \end{pmatrix}$

Exercise 12.13. Show that $\sum_{i=0}^{4} a_i y^i$, $a_4 = 1$, is the characteristic polynomial $C_A(y)$ of the following matrix A. (This can be generalized to any n.)

$$\begin{pmatrix} 0 & 1 & 0 & 0 \\ 0 & 0 & 1 & 0 \\ 0 & 0 & 0 & 1 \\ -a_0 & -a_1 & -a_2 & -a_3 \end{pmatrix}$$

MATRIC POLYNOMIALS

Since we shall ultimately be concerned with polynomials over a subset of $\mathscr{M}(\mathscr{F})$, we shall now consider polynomials over $\mathscr{M}_n(\mathscr{F})$. Such *matric polynomials* are polynomials in x whose coefficients are $n \times n$ matrices over $\mathscr{F}$. They can also be considered as matrices whose elements are polynomials in x over $\mathscr{F}$. For example,

$$\begin{pmatrix} 1 & 0 \\ -1 & 1 \end{pmatrix} + \begin{pmatrix} 2 & 1 \\ 1 & -1 \end{pmatrix} x + \begin{pmatrix} 3 & -2 \\ 1 & 1 \end{pmatrix} x^2$$
$$= \begin{pmatrix} 1 + 2x + 3x^2 & x - 2x^2 \\ -1 + x + x^2 & 1 - x + x^2 \end{pmatrix} \quad (1)$$

We shall be concerned with evaluating matric polynomials for particular values of x taken from $\mathscr{F}$ or $\mathscr{M}_n(\mathscr{F})$. A value for x from $\mathscr{F}$ may be substituted in either side of equation (1) with the same result (a 2×2 matrix). However, in substituting a matrix value for x we must use the form of the polynomial on the left side of equation (1).

Since matrix multiplication is not commutative, substitution of a matrix for x in Ax and in xA will not, in general, give the same result. For $P(x) = \sum_{i=0}^{k} A_i x^i$ we shall define a left value $P_L(C) = \sum_{i=0}^{k} C^i A_i$ and a right value $P_R(C) = \sum_{i=0}^{k} A_i C^i$.

▶**THEOREM 12.16.** Let $P(h,x) \, Q(j,x) = R(k,x)$, where P, Q, and R are matric polynomials and $k \leq h + j$. If $P_L(C) = Z$, then $R_L(C) = Z$.

PROOF: Let $P(x) = \sum_{i=0}^{h} A_i x^i$ and $Q(x) = \sum_{i=0}^{j} B_i x^i$. Then $R_L(C)$
$= A_0 B_0 + C(A_0 B_1 + A_1 B_0) + C^2(A_0 B_2 + A_1 B_1 + A_2 B_0)$
$+ \ldots + C^{h+j} A_h B_j = (A_0 + C A_1 + C^2 A_2 + \ldots + C^h A_h) B_0$
$+ C(A_0 + C A_1 + C^2 A_2 + \ldots + C^h A_h) B_1 + C^2(A_0 + C A_1$
$+ C^2 A_2 + \ldots + C^h A_h) B_2 + \ldots + C^j(A_0 + C A_1 + C^2 A_2$
$+ \ldots + C^h A_h) B_j = P_L(C) B_0 + C P_L(C) B_1 + C^2 P_L(C) B_2$
$+ \ldots + C^j P_L(C) B_j = Z$.

Exercise 12.14. If in Theorem 12.16 $Q_L(C) = Z$, show that $R_L(C) = Z$ does not necessarily follow.
$\left(\text{Hint: Use } P(x) = x\begin{pmatrix} 0 & 1 \\ 1 & 1 \end{pmatrix}, \; Q(x) = x\begin{pmatrix} 1 & 0 \\ 0 & 0 \end{pmatrix}, \text{ and } C = \begin{pmatrix} 0 & 1 \\ 0 & 1 \end{pmatrix}. \right)$

MINIMUM POLYNOMIALS

▶**THEOREM 12.17.** (Cayley-Hamilton.) Every matrix satisfies its characteristic equation.

PROOF: Substituting $y = A$ into the identity $(yI - A) \text{ adj}(yI - A) = \det(yI - A)I = C_A(y)I$, we obtain by Theorem 12.16 $C_A(A)I = Z$, whence $C_A(A) = Z$.

By Theorem 12.17 every matrix satisfies a polynomial equation of degree n. It is possible, however, that a particular matrix satisfies a polynomial equation of degree less than n. For example, the matrix I_n has as its characteristic equation $(y - y^0)^n = 0$, but also satisfies $y - y^0 = 0$.

▶**DEFINITION 12.6.** ‑ The lowest degree polynomial $M_A(y) = \sum_{i=0}^{k} a_i y^i$, with $a_k = 1$, for which $M_A(A) = Z$, is called the *minimum polynomial* of A.

▶**THEOREM 12.18.** Any polynomial $P(y)$ for which $P(A) = Z$ is a polynomial multiple of $M_A(y)$.

PROOF: By the division algorithm $P(y) = Q(y)M_A(y) + R(y)$ with the degree of $R(y)$ less than k. Substituting A, we obtain $Z = P(A) = Q(A)Z + R(A)$. Thus $R(A) = Z$, a contradiction to the definition of $M_A(y)$.

▶**COROLLARY 1.** The minimum polynomial of a matrix is unique.

▶**COROLLARY 2.** The roots of $M_A(y) = 0$ are characteristic values of A.

In the proof of Theorem 4.15 we used the first $n^2 + 1$ powers of a matrix A to establish a linear dependence. It is now obvious that a maximum of $k + 1$ powers would have been sufficient.

▶**THEOREM 12.19.** Every characteristic value is a root of $M_A(y) = 0$.

PROOF: Let y_i be a characteristic value of A and ξ_i a corresponding characteristic vector. By the division algorithm

$M_A(y) = Q(y)(y - y_i) + M_A(y_i)$. Substituting $y = A$ and multiplying by ξ_i^T, we obtain $M_A(A)\xi_i^T = Q(A)(A - y_iI)\xi_i^T + M_A(y_i)I\xi_i^T$. But by Definition 12.6 and Theorem 12.15 we have $M_A(A) = Z$ and $(A - y_iI)\xi_i^T = Z$. Thus $M_A(y_i)I\xi_i^T = Z$, and since $\xi_i \neq \epsilon_0$, we have $M_A(y_i) = 0$.

Exercise 12.15. Find $M_A(y)$ for the matrices in Exercise 12.9 and Exercise 12.10.

Exercise 12.16. Show that there exists an integer m such that $[M_A(y)]^m$ is a polynomial multiple of $C_A(y)$.

Exercise 12.17. Show that for A in Exercise 12.13 $M_A(y) = C_A(y)$. (*Hint:* Consider the first rows of the powers of A.)

Bibliography

Albert, A. A., *Modern Higher Algebra,* University of Chicago Press, Chicago, 1937.

Amir-Moez, A. R., and Fass, A. L., *Elements of Linear Spaces,* Edward Bros., Ann Arbor, Michigan, 1961.

Andree, Richard V., *Selections from Modern Abstract Algebra,* Holt, New York, 1958.

Beaumont, R. A., and Ball, R. W., *Introduction to Modern Algebra and Matrix Theory,* Rinehart, 1954.

Bellman, R., *Introduction to Matrix Analysis,* McGraw-Hill, New York, 1960.

Birkhoff, G., and MacLane, Saunders, *A Survey of Modern Algebra,* Revised Edition, Macmillan, New York, 1953.

Bocher, M., *Introduction to Higher Algebra,* Macmillan, New York, 1930.

Dickson, L. E., *New First Course in the Theory of Equations,* Wiley, New York, 1939.

Ficken, F. A., *The Simplex Method of Linear Programming,* Holt, Rinehart & Winston, 1961.

Garvin, W. W., *Introduction to Linear Programming,* McGraw-Hill, New York, 1960.

Gass, S. I., *Linear Programming,* McGraw-Hill, New York, 1958.

Hadley, G., *Linear Algebra,* Addison-Wesley, Reading, Mass., 1961.

Hadley, G., *Linear Programming,* Addison-Wesley, Reading, Mass., 1961.

Halmos, Paul R., *Finite Dimensional Vector Spaces,* Princeton University Press, Princeton, 1942.

Hoffman, K., and Kunze, R., *Linear Algebra,* Prentice-Hall, Englewood Cliffs, N.J., 1961.

Hohn, F. E., *Applied Boolean Algebra,* Macmillan, New York, 1960.

Hohn, F. E., *Elementary Matrix Algebra,* Macmillan, New York, 1958.

Jacobson, N., *Lectures in Abstract Algebra,* Vol. I, Van Nostrand, 1951.

Johnson, R. E., *First Course in Abstract Algebra,* Prentice-Hall, Englewood Cliffs, N.J., 1953.

McCoy, Neal H., *Introduction to Modern Algebra,* Allyn & Bacon, Boston, 1960.

MacDuffee, C. C., *An Introduction to Abstract Algebra,* Wiley, New York, 1953.

MacDuffee, C. C., *Vectors and Matrices,* Carus Mathematical Monograph, No. 7, The Mathematical Association of America, 1943.

Miller, K. S., *Elements of Modern Abstract Algebra,* Harper, New York, 1958.

Murdoch, D. C., *Linear Algebra for Undergraduates,* Wiley, New York, 1957.

Parker, W. V., and Eaves, J. C., *Matrices,* Ronald, New York, 1960.

Perlis, S., *Theory of Matrices,* Addison-Wesley, Reading, Mass., 1952.

Schreier, O., and Sperner, E., *Introduction to Modern Algebra and Matrix Theory,* Chelsea, New York, 1951.

Schwartz, J. T., *Matrices and Vectors,* McGraw-Hill, New York, 1961.

Schwerdtfeger, H., *Introduction to Linear Algebra and the Theory of Matrices,* P. Noordhoff N. V., Groningen, 1950.

Stoll, R. R., *Linear Algebra and Matrix Theory,* McGraw-Hill, New York, 1952.

Thrall, R. M., *Vector Spaces and Matrices,* Wiley, New York, 1957.

Vajda, S., *Mathematical Programming,* Addison-Wesley, Reading, Mass., 1961.

Van der Waerden, B. L., *Modern Algebra,* Ungar, New York, Vol. I, 1949, Vol. II, 1950.

Whitesitt, J. E., *Boolean Algebra and Its Applications,* Addison-Wesley, Reading, Mass., 1961.

Index

Numbers refer to pages.

List of Symbols

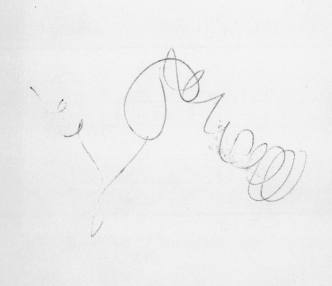